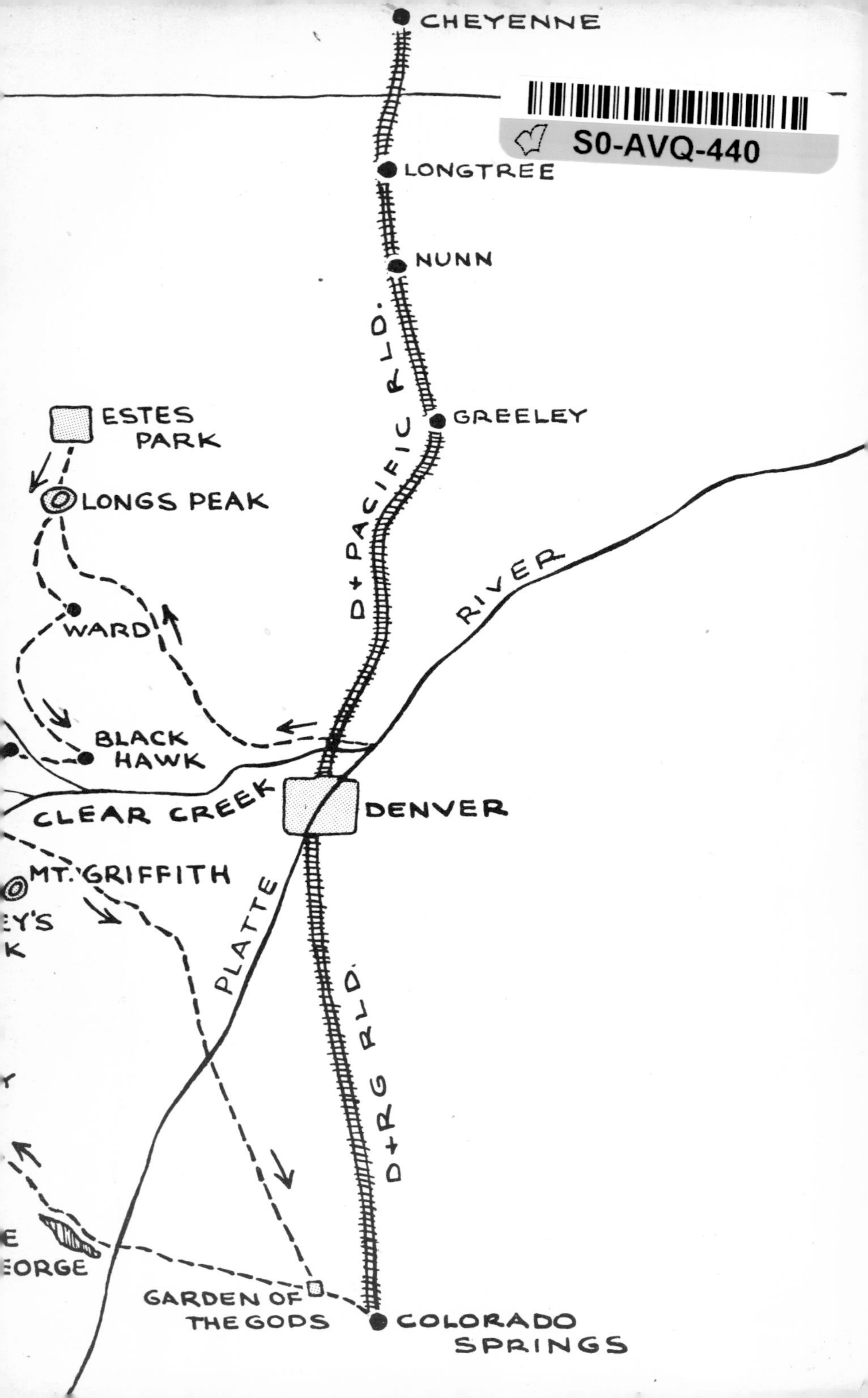

CHEYENNE

LONGTREE

NUNN

GREELEY

D + PACIFIC R.L.D.

RIVER

ESTES PARK

LONGS PEAK

WARD

BLACK HAWK

CLEAR CREEK

DENVER

MT. GRIFFITH

EY'S
K

PLATTE

D + R G R.L.D.

E
EORGE

GARDEN OF
THE GODS

COLORADO
SPRINGS

Quest

of the

SNOWY CROSS

CLARENCE S. JACKSON

LAWRENCE W. MARSHALL

University of Denver Press

Dedicated

to the memory of

DR. FERDINAND VANDIVEER HAYDEN

eminent geologist and director of the United States Geological Survey that bore his name, by whose wisdom and foresight photography was first employed to record the scenes and events of his several governmental expeditions into the West

and to

THE FIELD MEN

who served with him in the memorable Survey of 1873, whose courage, fidelity and ability to overcome difficulties contributed to the great story which is America's.

Quest
of the
SNOWY CROSS

CLARENCE S. JACKSON
LAWRENCE W. MARSHALL

In the year 1873 many men had heard from other men of the strange mountain in the West with the snowy cross on its side, but few of these men could lay claim to having actually seen the mountain. It remained for William H. Jackson, already famous for his pictures of the Yellowstone, to prove to the doubting Thomases that the Mount of the Holy Cross was no myth.

Here, told for the most part from the William H. Jackson diaries of that year, is the authentic story of the search for the snowy cross and of the achievement of the picture which even today still remains the best ever obtained of the Mount of the Holy Cross.

Illustrated with other pictures taken by Jackson on the 1873 Survey and with reproductions of famous paintings of the Mount of the Holy Cross.

FOREWORD

There is a mountain in the distant West
That, sun-defying, in its deep ravines
Displays a cross of snow upon its side.

Thus wrote Longfellow in 1879, but a few years earlier reports of the mountain to which he refers were received with skepticism. Repeatedly the tales of trapper and prospector have been dismissed as exaggeration if not downright fiction, only to stand vindicated later. It was a governmental expedition that, in 1873, brought back from the little-known fastness of central Colorado information concerning this mysterious mountain. Its strange and mystical beauty for the first time became widely known through reproduction of photographs by William H. Jackson and paintings, lithographs, and etchings by Thomas Moran. Inevitably it captured public imagination. With the lapse of years the fame of the Mount of the Holy Cross has in no wise diminished.

This remarkable peak is located fourteen miles northwest of the Continental Divide at Tennessee Pass, and gives its name to a National Forest which embraces it. It is most conveniently reached from points in Eagle River Cañon, seven miles northeast, which is traversed by the main line of the Denver & Rio Grande Western railroad, and by a principal highway. Redcliff and Minturn are cañon towns from which trips to the peak are usually made.

The peak is carved from the east side of a spur extending northward from the main body of the range, and it faces toward the northeast, across the east head of Cross Creek Cañon. ("Cross Creek Cañon" is the

7

"Roche Moutonnée Cañon" of the Hayden Survey maps.) Its distinctive outlines make the mountain easy to identify as far as it is visible, but glimpses of the east-northeast face, on which is graven the cross, are peculiarly elusive. By far the best view is that from Notch Mountain, a high point (about 13,200 feet) on the ridge directly across the cañon and squarely facing the cross. From more remote points this ridge looms up between the observer and the cross face, cutting off the view. Fortunately, there are a few stations sufficiently high so that one can look *over* the ridge and obtain a full view of the cross; in such views Notch Mountain merges with the lower slopes of the Mount and becomes indistinguishable. Probably the best of these rare stations is Shrine Pass, at the head of Turkey Creek, seven miles northeast of Redcliff and thirteen miles distant from the peak. Under favorable conditions the cross is distinctly seen from the vicinity of Loveland Pass and from Gray's Peak, though from this distance it becomes a subordinate feature almost lost among the myriad details of Colorado's skyline.

Heroic indeed are the proportions of the Cross of Snow. The couloir which forms the upright is about 1,150 feet long. Its depth varies from 25 to 125 feet, being greatest just below the crossarm. Inwardly the couloir narrows to a mere gash. It is difficult to estimate to what depth snow accumulates in it in winter. This couloir has formed along the outcrop of a vertical zone of yellowish schist which, being much less resistant than the gneiss on either side, has weathered out into a cleft. The arms of the cross are formed by an outward-sloping bench on the face of the mountain. It is 25 to 50 feet wide, and intersects the upright about 500 feet below its top. One can only estimate how far out from the

8

upright snow may at times lie on this bench; probably in most summers each arm is 200 feet or more long. The arms do not extend out from the upright exactly at right angles, but each is slightly lifted.

Claims that the discovery of the Mount of the Holy Cross may have been made as early as in the 16th century by Spanish explorers under Coronado have, apparently, little historic foundation and must therefore be regarded simply as interesting speculations. Similarly "early legends" about this peak which have been persistently circulated are so palpably made-to-order as to be wholly unconvincing, even as fiction.

As a matter of fact the mountain does not emerge from obscurity until 1869. On August 29 of that year William H. Brewer and several companions ascended Gray's Peak and subsequently in describing the summit view, Brewer noted that the Mount of the Holy Cross could be seen forty miles away, "with its cross of pure white, a mile high, suspended against its side." This reference to the peak and the cross is from one of Brewer's letters to his wife. The casual character of these early references implies that by 1869 the Mount of the Holy Cross was generally known and its name already established.

Enos Mills credits William N. Byers, founder of the *Rocky Mountain News* of Denver, with having made the first ascent of the Mount of the Holy Cross, but this bare statement, unsupported elsewhere so far as known, has been generally discounted. In his monograph ("Fourteen Thousand Feet") on the Colorado peaks, Hart is probably justified in ignoring this claim in favor of that of the Hayden party of 1873 which now engages our attention.

The personnel of this historic expedition included

9

an imposing array of distinguished scientists: F. V. Hayden, geologist and director of the Survey of the territories; William H. Jackson, artist and photographer; W. H. Holmes, artist and scientist; J. T. Gardner, topographer; W. D. Whitney, geologist; and John Coulter, botanist. These men, who in scattered parties had been engaged in exploring the mountains of central Colorado, on August 17 assembled with their assistants and pack outfits in the upper Arkansas Valley for the express purpose of making an expedition to the Mount of the Holy Cross. Gardner, as chief topographer, was then engaged in making primary triangulations from the highest peaks, preliminary to detailed mapping, and had selected the Mount of the Holy Cross for a station. His assistants had repeatedly located the peak from distant summits, and though reports concerning the cross were current, no one could be found who had actually seen it. Naturally the attainment of this mysterious peak proved no small adventure, even for these seasoned mountaineers.

Jackson's photographs, though made by the primitive wet plate methods of the time, are still generally regarded as the best ever obtained of the Mount of the Holy Cross. They were taken on the summit of Notch Mountain where Jackson sensitized, exposed, developed, and rinsed one 11 x 14 and seven 5 x 8 plates.

The actual ascent of the Mount of the Holy Cross had been completed by only Holmes and Gardner of the topographical division (presumably by way of the north ridge), and Gardner was elated at having "succeeded in getting splendid observations." He added, "We are undoubtedly the first who ever reached this peak," and in a letter dated August 24, Whitney wrote, "The Mount of the Holy Cross has been thoroughly done at last, but

10

at a cost of time and labor which was not at all antici-
pated. . . ."

During the period of western exploration no one
was more zealous in seeking out and making known to
the world at large the wonders of the Great West than
the eminent artist, Thomas Moran. In 1873 he had been
prevented from participating in the exploration just
recounted since that season he was in company with
John W. Powell in the Grand Canyon region. However,
the summer of 1874 found him in Colorado, eager to
paint the unique mountain which had been so glowingly
described by his colleagues on the Hayden Surveys. The
work which resulted, "The Mount of the Holy Cross,
Colorado," is conceded to be one of Moran's greatest
paintings and was awarded a medal and diploma at the
Centennial of 1876. In view of the difficulties experienced
by the 1873 party in reaching the Mount of the Holy
Cross it was at first thought that Moran himself probably did not get to see the peak at close range and that
he had depended solely upon Jackson's photographs for
his interpretations of the peak itself. However, a letter
has been discovered from Moran to his wife, written
August 24, 1874, in which he recounts the difficult climb
he and his men had just made up Notch Mountain to get
the magnificent view of the Cross.

Moran's painting was subsequently purchased by
a friend, Dr. William A. Bell, engineer with the D. & R.
G. W. railroad, and it hung in Dr. Bell's home at Manitou, Colorado, up to about 1905 when the owner, at his
retirement, took it with him to England. It is now in
the family estate, Pendell Court, Bletchingly, Surrey,
England. The removal of this painting, probably the
most famous yet made of an American mountain, has
naturally been a source of regret to many Americans.

The unique character of the Mount of the Holy Cross was brought to general attention on May 11, 1929, on which date President Herbert Hoover issued a proclamation establishing the Holy Cross National Monument, embracing an area of approximately 1,392 acres on and adjacent to the noted peak. Religious pilgrimages to the Mount of the Holy Cross have received much publicity. The Mount is credited with an imposing number of "miraculous cures" by "faith healing" and at one time a Denver pastor introduced the practice of "handkerchief healing" for the sick unable to make the pilgrimages.

Great is the debt of gratitude our own generation of mountain lovers owes to the artists, Jackson and Moran, who first proved the existence of the impressive snowy cross. The difficulties under which they carried on their pioneer work would have dismayed men of lesser stature and inspiration, and we must marvel that neither inclement seasons nor the hardships of mountain life ever seemed to deter them greatly, or dampen their ardor.

FRITIOF FRYXELL

ACKNOWLEDGMENT

The authors are most grateful to the many persons who aided in the preparation of this book and encouraged us in its completion—particularly to Miss Ina Auls, Director of the Western History Section of the Denver Public Library, for placing books, treatises and newspapers at our disposal and whose unlimited knowledge of the West she shared so freely; to Dr. LeRoy Hafen, Colorado State Historian, Mrs. Agnes Wright Spring, Executive Assistant to the President of the State Historical Society and to Mrs. Frances Shea, Librarian of the Society, for the loan of the original Jackson diary and for manifold suggestions and courtesies extended; to Mrs. Dolores Renze, State Archivist for the loan of prints, for illustrations from the original Survey negatives; to Elmer Owen, Postmaster at Minturn, Colorado, for making it possible for us to be present at and to participate in the ceremonies attending the sale of the first cover issue of Colorado's Seventy-fifth Anniversary Commemorative Stamp; to Mrs. Ethel Bayer, of Minturn, for so amply adding to our knowledge of the terrain and history of the region surrounding the Mount of the Holy Cross; to Mr. and Mrs. William North of Leadville for performing a similar service regarding the Oro City-California Gulch country; to Mr. and Mrs. Andrew Demo of Colorado Springs with whom we traversed much of the ground traveled by the Survey party of 1873; and to George M. Osborne for his painstaking criticism and guidance throughout the writing of the manuscript. We are especially indebted to Herndon Davis, eminent Western artist, whose sketches adorn the chapter headings of this book.

ILLUSTRATIONS

All photographs, unless otherwise marked, are from the original William H. Jackson negatives, courtesy of the United States Department of the Interior.

Oft in the stilly night,
  Ere slumber's chain has bound me,
Fond Memory brings the light
  Of other days around me.

One evening, toward the middle of August, 1893,
the Jackson family was gathered in the library and livingroom of our home in Denver. William H. Jackson,
my father, was assiduously perusing the *Republican* for
news of the panic that had hit the country that year.
. . . Emilie, my mother, was knitting . . . Louise, one

17

of my sisters, was thrumming on the piano . . . Hallie, my other sister, played with her dolls on the floor . . . and I? Well, I hardly remember exactly what I was doing as a boy of seventeen. All was peaceful and quiet, except for the noise Louise was making at the piano, which, as I well remember, greatly annoyed me.

Suddenly, the door bell rang. Louise jumped up and started for the door, with father close behind her.

From where I was, I could hear him warmly greet two old friends—Charlie Hooper, son of S. K. Hooper, G. P. A. of the Denver and Rio Grande Railroad and Bertram Wentworth, a clerk in the First National Bank and an enthusiastic amateur photographer.

It was not long after we were seated again that they announced the purpose of their visit. They reminded father (as if he didn't know) that the 23rd of the month would be the twentieth anniversary of his first photographing the now famous Mount of the Holy Cross. And they thought it would be a wonderful idea to re-enact the climb and make some new photographs.

The amazing symbol of the Christian faith, etched in lines of eternal snow upon the face of the mountain peak, had become well known during the last twenty years, principally through father's photographs, but also through several great paintings, by such artists as Thomas Moran and W. H. Holmes (late Director of the National Art Gallery in Washington, D. C.), and through verses and poems written about it—notably one by Henry W. Longfellow in 1879.

The idea struck father as particularly interesting and he was immediately for it. All ears, I listened and hoped I would be included in the party. I had just finished my schooling in the East and was working in my father's studio at 13th and Colfax. And I was eager to test my legs and wind in a serious mountain climb.

18

Although I knew of the existence of this phenomenon of nature through making many albumen prints from negatives, I knew nothing of the story of that first adventure that brought the marvel, through photography, to the attention of the country.

Before the guests left, two hours later, they had completed plans for the trip and a very delighted boy had been invited to join the party.

On the evening of August 22nd we four boarded the train at Union Depot. The men, well-equipped with climbing poles and outfitted properly, were in severe contrast to me, tagging along in everyday clothes. Imagine! I even sported a new Fedora hat.

Before daylight the next morning, we were routed out of comfortable berths by the porter who announced the train would soon stop (by special arrangment with the Passenger Department) at a siding in Eagle Canyon. From there, we were to begin the perilous climb. There was no time for breakfast—just enough to hustle into our clothes and get out on the tracks in the cool crisp dawn of a perfect day.

We watched the train move on and soon disappear down the canyon; then we gathered up our packs. On the left, across the roaring Eagle River, were sheer cliffs with no indication of a trail to the summit. A rickety rope bridge spanned the stream, and, led by father, we cautiously scrambled across in Indian file.

But father knew where the trail was hidden—he had been there before—and soon we rested on the rim of the canyon and prepared a light breakfast. The sun came up, touching the snow-capped peaks and hills, casting that delightful early morning glow upon the wilderness before us. The air was clear and crisp. From our location, we could see the lovely pyramid-shaped

19

peak in the distance, but no cross of snow. That was facing east into the rising sun.

Led by father, we started out, beating our way over fallen timber and huge rocks for a mile or two until we came to a dense thicket of chapparal into which we plunged. It was hard work bending the tough reeds aside for a path, but soon a clearing appeared beside a small mountain stream. Here, we halted for a much-needed rest.

While we were resting, father wandered about the clearing, apparently looking for something. His actions aroused the curiosity of both Charlie and Bert who inquired what it was he was hunting. Father told them that he remembered this exact spot as one where his photographic party had camped in '73. Later, he proved it as he showed us a small pine tree with a short section of stovepipe around its base. He explained that this metal band had been placed around the tree when they broke camp, twenty years before. And it was still in place, rusted but not disintegrated, and held more tightly in place by the expanded tree trunk.

From this point, the climbing became increasingly difficult up the steep sides of Notch Mountain with no trail to guide us. On every rise pine needles caused us to slip back one foot for every two forward, or so it seemed. Bare rocks and boulders were now in evidence as we reached timberline (10,000 feet) and little patches of glacial snow showed up frequently in our path. Each of us was carrying some weight, either in utensils, food, or photographic equipment. I, of course, was given a light load and this encouraged me to spurt ahead of the others in order to have the distinction of reaching the summit first.

I was warned to "take it easy" in the high altitude, but a young, strong, and eager youth is not inclined to heed warnings. I called back, "See you at the top" and went boldly ahead, scrambling like a mountain goat over the jagged rocks, getting more and more excited as I proceeded. Then, suddenly, I came to a ledge, and there before my eyes was the famous peak with its almost perfect cross of snow glistening in the sunlight of midday.

It was a thrilling sight—one I shall never forget as long as I live—and I momentarily halted and unconsciously bowed my head in boyish reverence. I couldn't see the others, who were far behind "taking it easy," so I scrambled on and in another half hour had reached the summit of Notch Mountain.

Here, at the very spot from which the first photographs were made, I sat down, weary and tired, admiring the grandeur of the panorama before my eyes. From where I sat, I tossed a stone over the precipice. It fell a thousand feet down, where I could hear it rumble as it started other rocks in a miniature slide. It was becoming warm in the sun and I relaxed, waiting for the others who appeared in a few moments.

They discarded their packs and took up seated positions in a little group, silently gazing at the marvelous spectacle before us. None of us except father had ever seen the cross of snow before. Its vast majesty silenced all talk for the moment.

Then father spoke. He told us the story—new to all of us—of his first visit to this spot, and we listened in solemn attention. He remembered the vastly different conditions twenty years before when he stood at this same position, surrounded by a sea of swirling clouds, his photographic outfit packed away in utter discouragement and disappointment—he could not even see the outlines of the peak across the deep gulch that separated it from Notch Mountain. But the part of the story that interested me most was how he had been granted a preview as he started back to timberline camp where his companions had foundered under their heavy loads.

A clap of lightning, he said, and a roll of thunder had preceded a sudden rift in the clouds. Then, as though some unseen hand had pulled aside the curtain, he saw the sunlit peak with its snowy cross glistening like a million diamonds in the center of an iris diaphragm. He had no chance to coat plates or make exposures, so he just stood there, arms folded, regretting his fate in not being able to record the amazing spectacle. In a moment, the show was over and he slowly descended to camp.

I pondered this part of the story in my youthful fashion and regretted, I think, even more than the others that this miracle in the clouds could not have been recorded. The more I thought, the more determined I was to do something about it.

It was almost three o'clock when we started back and little did we know how much more difficult and tiring was the descent than the ascent. To make matters worse, Charlie Hooper fell on a jagged rock and sprained his ankle, necessitating his being partly carried down the steep incline in great pain. Shadows began to fall and it was soon dark, with only the outlines of the hills in view. The rugged going had us completely fagged out as we came upon the last descent of the cliff to the river and the railroad tracks.

But we made it, thanks to the unerring guidance of the old pioneer. By special arrangement, the train from Salt Lake City was ordered to stop for us and four weary mountain climbers piled into comfortable berths about as quickly as they could shed their clothes.

About two weeks later I was printing pictures on the roof of our building in Denver, still pondering the

22

problem of how to represent in a composite photograph what my father had seen that fateful day. Clouds were swirling overhead, tumbling about, making many curious formations. I rushed inside and got a camera, pointed it into the sky . . . and waited. I was rewarded shortly by seeing an opening which I judged similar to the one through which father had viewed the snowy cross. I snapped the picture and feverishly developed it.

It was perfect—perfect in the opportunity it presented for vignetting father's original negative of the Mt. of the Holy Cross and mine of the clouds into a composite picture. Father saw it and was greatly moved that I should have been the one to visualize what he had seen but had been unable to record.

That is the story behind the picture with the clouds, but the story of father's original photograph is a far greater one.

Beautiful dreamer, queen of my song,
List while I woo thee with soft melody:
Gone are the cares of life's busy throng
Beautiful dreamer, awake unto me,
Beautiful dreamer, awake unto me.

William H. Jackson was at complete and unalloyed peace with the world as he loped along on his horse Chipper over the prairie trail from the Omaha Indian Agency to Omaha. He laughed aloud as he thought of yesterday, how he had been a trifle apprehensive over the reaction he might receive to that important question

25

he had asked of Emilie. Now—the most wonderful girl in the world had promised to be his forever. And everyone—Emilie, her parents, and the Indians at the Agency —rejoiced with him at the successful outcome of his suit. What man, he wondered, ever had a greater inspiration for fulfillment of his big dream than he did.

"Emilie." He spoke the name aloud and Chipper snorted in answering good spirits. "Emilie." He remembered her understanding sympathy for his great search, his "Holy Grail"—the mysterious mountain in Colorado said to bear on its rocky slope a massive cross of snow. How much easier his leave-taking had been, knowing she understood and believed in his search. Now, on his way to join the Hayden Survey, he pledged himself to find the mountain and photograph it—for Emilie—hearing again her voice, trembling with emotion, "God placed that cross of snow as a symbol and the world must be able to see its beauty. I know thee will be the one to make that possible."

The fog horn "to-o-o-t, to-o-ot" of an occasional river boat broke into his reverie. He was nearing the wide Missouri. On more familiar ground now, Chipper strained at the reins and Jackson had to pull up hard and talk fast to hold the animal in check. Within minutes they pulled up at the livery stable. Jackson paid his bill and took from the saddle bags his personal belongings and the precious box of lunch Emilie's mother had sent with him. With these rolled under his arm, he made his way across to the station. With an hour to kill, he procured reading material — *The Omaha World, Leslie's Weekly, Scribner's Magazine* and *Harper's Weekly* — from the newsstand, and, occupied with these sat out the time in the dingy waiting room.

The train ride across Nebraska was uneventful. The prairie country along the U.P. route was old stuff to

26

Jackson. True, the Oregon Trail, over which he had traveled in other days, paralleled the route most of the distance across Nebraska Territory, and, from time to time, as he looked up from his reading, he could pick out some landmark to kindle a spark in his memory. The portion of the old trail he remembered best—the region embracing Chimney Rock and Scott's Bluff in the northwestern part of the Territory—the train would pass far to the south during the night, when he would be enjoying peaceful repose in a comfortable berth on one of the Pullmans the U.P. had recently added to its main line trains. Even the half-hour stopover, near Ogallala, to permit passengers to shoot buffalo from the train—a practice Jackson whole-heartedly deplored — would be omitted because the train would be passing the spot some time after midnight.

Reaching Cheyenne early the following morning, Jackson was glad for the two-hour layover which enabled him to stretch his legs, and to look over the rapidly growing town with which he had been so familiar when it was the "end of the line." As he walked up-town from the depot in search of a likely looking place for his breakfast, he marvelled at the remarkable change that had taken place in the past four or five years.

He thought of his own railroad days, when he was making pictures along the U.P. as it was being constructed; the trials and tribulations; his not too regular eating; his constant struggle to buy the necessary photographic equipment—those few pitiful orders for portraits from Cheyenne's shady ladies, particularly those in Madame Cleveland's establishment, which enabled him to continue in business a little longer.

The tents, which had been the only dwellings in those days, were gone, replaced by frame shacks and a few brick structures. The saloons, brothels, and gambling houses were still very much in evidence, gaudily and brazenly advertised. Legitimate business houses were much less striking, but he was pleased to note they had gained appreciably in numbers and sense of permanency. The prevalence of cowboys emphasized the fast growing cattle industry on these western plains. The huge, rambling stockyards, the many tanneries, the saddle and leather shops, the blacksmith shops and the score or more of veterinarians' offices stamped the place unmistakably as a cow town that would endure.

Jackson selected a neat little eating place—the Cowboy Lunch—gaudily bedecked inside and out with ranch scenes. As he sat down at a table and glanced about the room, he noted that some of the wall decorations were copies, crude to be sure, of his own widely known pictures. He felt slight elation that his work was thought good enough to copy and wondered if the pert little waitress would be in the least flustered if she should be informed that her customer was the original creator of the painted scenes which had become a part of her daily life.

The little three-coach train of the Denver and Pacific Railroad was made up and ready when Jackson approached the station, its tiny engine gurgling contentedly as it puffed up smoke clouds through its funnel-like smokestack. Jackson boarded the first of the two passenger cars, selected a seat toward the center, and, after placing his "carrying" valise in the rack above, settled back for some leisurely rest during the remaining few hours of his trip. The train chugged out of the station, giving a few uncertain snorts, then, as the chug-chugging leveled off and the train picked up momentum, Jackson's mind drifted on to thoughts of the future.

He'd be with his old pals for supper tonight, and that cheered him. He was anxious to get on with the summer's work and back to Emilie. What did the summer have in store? He mused sleepily, lulled gently by the swaying of the train. What-did-the-summer-have-in-store? The Indians—the Cheyennes—were they as obstreperous as their brothers in Wyoming who had been the cause of Hayden changing his plans for '73? Wouldn't that be something—to find himself in the midst of an Indian uprising, he, a full-fledged member of the Omaha tribe! He'd better not even mention that possibility to Emilie. He peered out the window. What God-forsaken place was this? Must be Lone Tree.

The train resumed its chugging southward and Jackson sank back once again. What did Dr. Hayden have up his sleeve for this summer? Work east of the Divide —that was a big order. He knew Dr. Hayden had been greatly disturbed by the fact that the people were getting erroneous impressions of the West and that he wanted, by the use of photography, to tell the story truthfully. He remembered the day Dr. Hayden had come in to the printing room in Washington, calling excitedly "Jack! Jack! I've got news—great news!" Congress had passed the increased appropriation for the Geological Survey of 1873. The go-ahead. It was only because of that appropriation that he was here now.

The train jerked to a halt at Nunn. It had not yet attained the status of a "wide spot in the road."

"By George," Jackson thought, almost aloud, "this little road can't expect much revenue from these tiny stops. Must depend on business from its two terminals." He looked about the car as the train rattled on to its next destination. "Pretty full, at that," he assured himself, "and that accommodation car certainly was chock full of stuff. I don't think Governor Evans and the other good people down in Denver, who put up the money for this road, are losing money."

He met the eye of the passenger across the aisle. Pretty eyes, too, he thought, and then turned away his gaze as quickly as he had looked up. He just wasn't staring at women—not even beautiful ones. Anyway this one couldn't hold a candle to Emilie. No one could.

"Mr. Jackson," he heard her say pleasantly, and he cast a startled look toward her, "could you open this window a little for me?"

"Wh-hy certainly," he stammered, getting to his feet and stepping across the aisle to tackle the coach window. After a few grunts and tugs, the window grudgingly opened a foot or more and several weeks' accumulation of soot and cinders blew over the lady he was trying to assist.

"Oh, dear," she choked and flitted a dainty lace kerchief to her nose.

Jackson hurriedly pulled the window down and stuttered apologies. He used his own handkerchief as a duster and deftly wiped off the dust from the window sill and seat.

The lady thanked him and slid over toward the window. Jackson took the hint, not without some apprehension that perhaps this was not accepted conduct for a man just engaged. He sat down beside her.

"You-you called my name, madame," he said, "but you have me at a disadvantage, Miss . . . ah . . . Miss—"

"*Mrs.* Curtis," she supplied, correcting his hesitant inquiry.

"I am delighted to meet you, *Mrs.* Curtis. But, please, how in the world did you know my name?"

"Do young men who are traveling put other names than their own on their valises?" she laughingly inquired.

"Well, I'll be . . . jiggered!" he ejaculated. "And here I was beginning to think you were a detective or a mind reader."

"Would you be further surprised if I asked you what part of Colorado the Hayden Survey intends to cover this year?"

"No, I really wouldn't for that U.S.G.S. on my baggage is pretty tell-tale."

"I can tell you also that our newspapers have been noting lately that the Hayden party is now concentrating near Denver, preparatory to an excursion into the nearby mountains."

Jackson told her briefly of his official position with the Survey and was surprised to find how well acquainted she was not only with Dr. Hayden, personally, but with his own photographic work of previous years in the Yellowstone. Her apparently unlimited knowledge of affairs rather exclusive with men folks of the day was somewhat explained when she volunteered:

"My husband is with the Land Office in Denver and keeps me posted on such matters. You'll have the pleasure of meeting him."

The rest of the trip into Denver was enlivened by sprightly conversation about Denver, railroads, the fast growing West and the challenge offered man by the innumerable mountain peaks looming in the western sky. Mrs. Curtis had heard of the illusive Snowy Cross, and hoped it would really be discovered and photographed some day. Jackson hoped he could accommodate her, but reminded himself that that was a command from Emilie who had prior claim to his activities in this particular case. When he told her of his recent engagement,

Mrs. Curtis uttered a delightful "how thrilling." She pledged him to call at the Curtis home in Denver for dinner and to meet her husband.

The little "puffer belly" engine chugged over the Platte river bridge and pulled into the Denver Union Depot. Bewhiskered men, top-hatted, weighted down with heavy watch chains, were on hand with hoop-skirted, gaily parasolled ladies to greet friends returning from Wyoming or making the adventurous journey to Denver for the first time. Jackson, struggling with his own and Mrs. Curtis' baggage, followed her out of the coach as she called "Oh, George, George. Here I am."

Jackson looked up to see a young, dark, handsome giant of a man eagerly searching the car exits for a glimpse of his lady. He quickly reached her side and lifted her off the platform in an embrace. Jackson deposited each article of baggage at their feet and awkwardly awaited developments.

"Oh, I'm so sorry," she gasped. "George, this is Mr. Jackson of the Hayden Survey. He has been so kind and helpful all the way from Cheyenne."

Both men shook hands warmly. Jackson instinctively felt a close kinship for the big man.

"The pleasure is all mine," Jackson managed to utter and immediately wondered if George might possibly detect a little too much ardor in that "all." But jealousy was no part of George's makeup and he was genuinely grateful that a fellow traveler had rendered assistance to his wife.

"And I have asked him to come to dinner at his first opportunity," Mrs. Curtis added.

George heartily endorsed the idea and Jackson promised that he would be happy to accept the very first day he was back in Denver.

Picture maker of the Old West.
From an oil painting by William H. Jackson.

Anniversary expedition to Mount of Holy Cross, August, 1893.
Left to right, Charlie Hooper, Clarence Jackson, Bertram Wentworth.

Another view of the anniversary expedition.

Long's Peak.

Camp Study.
Left to right, J. M. Coulter, Lt. Carpenter, two unnamed packers,
Potato John, and W. H. Jackson.

A panoramic view of the Front Range from Bald Mountain near Ward.

The packers and Jim Cole, right.

A heavy load on old Mag.

Looking away, Jackson saw another man approaching diffidently.

"Please pardon me," the man said, "but if you can spare Mr. Jackson, I should like to take him out to camp."

The speaker, a heavy-set, black-bearded man in a battered hat and baggy trousers, was in his early thirties, Jackson surmised. The man smiled and bowed to Mrs. Curtis, adding, "I am J. T. Gardner, topographer for the Hayden Survey, and by process of elimination I am quite certain this young man is the object of my journey in from Clear Creek Camp."

"Right you are, Mr. Gardner," Jackson said. "And I'm really glad to make your acquaintance. I've been looking forward to meeting you ever since Dr. Hayden told me we were to have a new topographer. And I'd like you to meet my new friends, Mr. and Mrs. Curtis."

There followed an exchange of the pleasures of meeting, added invitations to call, and then the Curtises withdrew via hack and Gardner and Jackson proceeded with the business of collecting Jackson's baggage.

For it's always fair weather
When good fellows get together,
With a stein on the table
And a good song ringing clear.

Jackson liked Gardner from the start. He had specu-
lated about him when he first learned from Dr. Hayden
that a new topographer was to be with him during the
coming season. He remembered that the Doctor had not,
as long as he had known him, made a mistake in picking
a man, and certainly he would not make one in selection

35

of a second in command. Now that he had met Gardner, he assured himself that his confidence in the Doctor's selections had not been misplaced.

Gardner had driven in from the base camp, "Clear Creek Camp"—at the junction of Clear Creek and the South Platte River—in the one light buckboard the Survey party owned. The two who were to become fast friends swapped inquiries while loading the buckboard with Jackson's materials and spoke enthusiastically of the work ahead. Gardner knew of the part Jackson's photographs had played in inducing Congress to create the first National Park in the Yellowstone and was lavish in his praise of his work. Jackson, in turn, knowing the wide reputation Gardner enjoyed as a topographer, was equally laudatory.

"I understand the Doctor has some wonderful new plans for all of us this year, too," Gardner volunteered as the buckboard, drawn by mares Jenny and Jill, holdovers from the '72 expedition, rattled over the bridge connecting the town of Highlands with Denver.

"And maybe you didn't know it," Gardner added, "but you're going to command a little party of your own this year. The Doctor is going to let you strike out for some of those tall peaks over there and shoot to your heart's content. You're to make a bee line for Long's Peak and then work down the Snowy Range to Gray's. Watch out for the toll-gate people at Georgetown—they're robbers. Argentine Pass will be easy. Work around by Pike's Peak and then cut across from there to meet the rest of us at Fairplay. We're to reach that point by July 10th, according to present plans."

"And then?" Jackson asked, admitting that Dr. Hayden had already given him an inkling of things to come.

"Only God and the Doctor knows. Have a hunch we'll work around to the headwaters of the Arkansas. And say, somewhere in that region, we're likely to run across that Snowy Cross mountain—you know, the one the Indians and trappers and prospectors tell such mysterious stories about. You've heard some of those wild tales, haven't you?"

Had he ever heard of the Cross of Snow? Had he ever heard of the moon? He was slightly startled at Gardner's surmise and subsequent query. The Snowy Cross was his—his and Emilie's. Hadn't he promised her he would discover and photograph it? And hadn't she promised to marry him this very year, confident he'd be successful? There was nothing else in the world so important to him. To do for the Mt. of the Holy Cross what he had done for the Yellowstone country—by his art of photography prove to the doubting Thomases that these nature myths were actually true!

Gardner's quick glance at Jackson, prompted by his failure to reply, aroused the latter from his reverie.

"Oh, yes, I've heard of it," he said casually.

"You don't seem very enthusiastic," Gardner prodded. "Sort of expected you to be elated. You're always so eager to get a picture no one else has made."

"Don't worry, J.T., if it's in Colorado, we'll find it."

Gardner, reassured by this apparent recapture of enthusiasm, did not press the matter further. Gardner had touched on the all-absorbing topic Jackson and Emilie had agreed was to be the great achievement this summer. Yet Jackson's natural modesty, closely bordering on reticence, forbade him to discuss with anyone the inspiration he had received to duplicate his accomplishments in the Yellowstone two years before. There was reason enough why some members of the Survey always

37

referred to him as "the man of few words."

As the buckboard rolled on through Garden Place and into Globeville, Gardner again jolted Jackson with: "By the way, Jack, did I make it clear you are *officially* in charge of the Photographic Division on this expedition? It's your party, boy. All yours."

"Yes, J.T., the Doctor gave me that good news in Washington. I've been thrilled as a child ever since." His party! He was really delighted with that prospect. It was all very well and pleasant to follow along with the Doctor and to hear at punctual intervals: "Here, Jack, get a picture of this," or "Can you make a good shot of that?" But to be on his own—to make what appeared worthwhile and proper, what appealed to the artist conscious of his duty on a scientific expedition. Yes, the world was great and wide and beautiful. Emilie, too, would be delighted that her Will had been given this important assignment and freedom to photograph what he desired. If only somehow he could stumble onto that illusive mountain that so many others had claimed always disappeared when one approached it. If the symbol of the Christian faith actually was etched in lines of snow on the summit of a high peak, what a marvelous phenomenon—what an inspiration to millions of devout people if they but could see a picture of it.

"Lift up thine eyes to the hills from which cometh thy help," that was what the Good Book said. To himself, he repeated the words over and over again.

Gardner interrupted, "I'm glad for your sake you can shoot anything you want, including that mountain."

"Thanks, J.T.," Jackson replied and again repeated, "if it's in Colorado, we'll find it."

Now within sight of Clear Creek Camp, Jackson could make out the customary pseudo-military geometric layout of all Dr. Hayden's base camps. There were the clean rows of white-wall tents as meticulous as any critical general could desire. Five tents to a row or street faced an equal number of tents opposite. Each division of the Survey was allotted ten tents, or one street, for men and equipment during their days at the base camp.

A few paces from one end of each street, and lined as carefully as the tents, were the open fire places for cooking. Near each of such fire places were mess tents, actually squares of canvas propped by four posts and affording top covering only. These, too, were arranged in a mathematically perfect line. Each contained an eight-foot table and benches on either side. Far to the opposite end of the streets were canvas enclosures, marking off and concealing man- and shovel-made excavations across which had been constructed stout but smooth pine boards with suitable openings at intervals, for the comfort of men who had business thereabout. And still farther out from these enclosures were the picket lines on which horses and mules were staked but with sufficient rope to permit free and easy grazing in the very immediate vicinity. The few vehicles belonging to the Survey were spotted, again in those precise rows, a few feet from the line of mess tents.

Jackson smiled wryly as he looked at this perfect camp and thought of the vast difference he and his men would encounter in their mode of living, once they "hit the trail" and the vicissitudes of terrain, weather, predatory animals and insects would determine the make-up of camps or bivouacs day by day.

When the buckboard unloaded its passengers and baggage at the base camp, the boys were about to sample some of Potato John's offerings for the evening meal.

The warm, if slightly ribald, greetings of these companions of previous expeditions gave Jackson that strong feeling of confidence that comes to a man only when surrounded by good and loyal friends.

"Hi there, Nitinah, how's the old Magic Eye?" called Lt. W. L. Carpenter, on leave from the army for work as entomologist for the Survey.

And then Coulter, the naturalist and avid prankster of the party, yelled, "Well, here's good old Jack again. What detained you? We thought you might have met some lady at the Omaha Indian Agency and decided to pay her court rather than photograph the wonders of this great West."

The color mounting to Jackson's cheeks gave all a hearty laugh. He wondered what Hayden could have told them about his request to visit in Omaha before coming West. Surely they could know nothing about Emilie.

He couldn't know that Coulter's remark was a shot in the dark—an innocent effort to get Jackson to be more voluble regarding his personal affairs. That blush of his was a dead give away as though he had shouted, "Boys, I've got a girl near Omaha and we're going to be married this fall." The general laughs going around the company plainly indicated who was going to be the butt of the jokes during the coming summer.

Potato John looked up from his work over the open-pit fire as Jackson approached and a wide grin spread over his usually solemn face. "Well, Mr. Jackson, I'm right glad to see you," he said, vigorously shaking his hand. "You sure look your old self. Just grab your share of the ground hereabouts and grub'll be up in no time."

The last portion of John's remarks was music to

Jackson's ears, for he had eaten nothing since his cowboy breakfast in Cheyenne.

Solemn old Potato John! To a newcomer, he appeared sour, cold, and crotchety—all six-foot-four of him. Any newcomer, however, within an hour or two after joining the party would learn that John was the life of it—philosopher, guitar player, story teller (whoppers). He was the man who could spit further than anyone in the group, who had a larger fund of words, descriptive and genealogical, to use in addressing the mules, and who could whip up a more palatable meal for discerning, hardy, outdoor men than any chef in the finest hotels in the land. Although the boys kidded him unmercifully, they admitted (privately and out of his hearing) there was no better cook in the country.

A young fellow Jackson had not met before was introduced as Jim Cole, son of a United States Senator from California, who had been allowed to join the Survey to further his study of birds. He was only seventeen years old, but a fine looking, slender, well-groomed youth, easily accepted as one of the group by this gathering of outdoor men. His insatiable desire to learn, coupled with innate modesty and demonstrated respect for the older and more experienced men made him popular with all.

Tom Cooper and Bill Whan, the "best damn packer in creation" (quoting Potato John), old Survey men and hence old friends of Jackson's, added their spicy greetings to those of the rest. Both were rough, grizzled old veterans of the trail, tried and true men who could be depended upon in any emergency. Jackson liked them immensely. They beamed with pride when he told them how glad he was to have them in his party.

It was good to be back. This little group included

41

some of the best scientific brains in the country, welded together by an unswerving loyalty to the Doctor and the Survey. They were not super men, neither saints nor devils, but men possessing their share of human failings, a large amount of courage and an oversupply of pride in their work for the U.S.G.S. These were the men who composed Jackson's party—the Photographic Division of the Hayden Survey of 1873. He was proud of them all—and he had the additional satisfaction that they extended the same loyalty to him that they did to Hayden.

There followed several days of preparation for the expedition. The pack animals and the riding mounts were selected with care. Each item of equipment was chosen with an eye to its absolute necessity, with considerable improvisation of utensils and equipage. The household article offered in the stores in Denver was not always adapted to mountain camping. The problems that arose enabled each specialist in the group to exercise inventive, mechanical, and artistic aptitudes on gadgets for use in his particular field. Many were the trips into Denver in those few days for realizations from blacksmith or foundry of this creative thinking.

Jackson introduced improvements in the packing of his photographic materials. This season he planned to carry his "studio" in *aparejos* on two mules and selected Gimlet and Hypo for this signal honor. Cooper and Whan practiced packing and unpacking Jackson's picture making stuff so long and so often they could produce the tiniest item from the inner depths of the *aparejo* in a little less than nothing flat. And it was well they could, for when Jackson decided to "make" or develop a picture, he demanded this or that in the same way a doctor commands nurses in the tenseness of a hospital operating room.

Jackson had been so occupied in these preparations he had all but forgotten the Curtises and their kind invitation. On the 22nd, when the work had progressed to the point where it was evident the photographic section would be ready to depart on time, he proposed to Gardner, who was in charge of the entire operations in Dr. Hayden's absence, that they drop into Denver and enjoy the Curtis' hospitality. Gardner was all for it, and early in the afternoon, the two buckboarded into town behind Jenny and Jill.

The thriving little city had progressed within the past three years, ending the era of oxen freighting eastward. Greatest growth was east of Cherry Creek. The 15,000 inhabitants lived in homes along streets and avenues stretching four miles to the east and two or more to the south. Larimer Street, running east and west through the heart of the city, was by far the most heavily trafficked, the widest, and had the finest shops. Beginning in old Auraria, across the creek, and extending westward, streets lettered from A to H bisected Larimer and composed the booming city's "downtown." Throughout its length, Larimer Street had fine wooden sidewalks with hitching posts before each house and business establishment. Gas lights illuminated the thoroughfare at night.

The buckboard rolled into the northeastern limits of Denver, traversed several blocks southward on York Street to Larimer, and thence to the downtown district along that thoroughfare. At the American House, they engaged a messenger to carry a note to Mrs. Curtis that they were in town and awaited her pleasure. Having received her response and word to be at her home at six o'clock, they availed themselves of the opportunity to see downtown Denver and to patronize the shops.

The matter of correspondence between Emilie and Jackson had been given due consideration. Before his departure, Jackson had given her the Ford House in Denver as his headquarters. On each previous trip into town, he had duly checked at the Ford House and just as often he had found waiting for him letters from Emilie—scented, inscribed on pink stationery and sealed with the Painter family wax seal, bearing the letter "P." It hardly need be said that the first stop in this "seeing Denver" tour with Gardner was the Ford House.

There, Gardner waited patiently and uncomplainingly while Jackson received his usual letter from a smiling clerk and buried himself in the latest news from the Omaha Agency. Upon finishing his delightful chore, Jackson beamed at Gardner and indicated that whatever Gardner wanted to see or do would be all right with him. His own personal business was concluded.

The two strolled down one side of Larimer Street as far as Ferry Street, across the creek and back on the other. They made side trips of a block or two along F and G Streets to appraise the newer buildings and stores. Having had not a single purchase in mind when they started out, in an amazingly short time they were loaded down with parcels. They couldn't resist buying articles of clothing at Daniel's and Fisher's elegant new department store, a large box of bon-bons (for Mrs. Curtis) at W. S. Cheeseman's Drug Store, a book or two and the latest periodicals at David Moffat's Book and Stationery Store, a few fancy groceries at Cornforth's Grocery.

They bought souvenir gifts for friends "back home" and trinkets they felt they might use themselves at some future date. Fortunately for them, their time downtown was running out and they had to call a halt to this shop-

44

ping orgy. They had barely enough time to post their gifts, check their parcels at the American House and endeavor to make themselves presentable.

Disdaining to ride the horsecar, which would have taken them almost to the Curtis home, they chose instead to use their own transportation. It was well they did, for Jenny and Jill, tied to a hitching post in front of the American House all this time, were getting rather tired of the whole thing. Promptly at six, they appeared at the Curtis home on Sherman Street where George Curtis greeted them at the door. Jenny and Jill were turned loose to stomp in the spacious picket-fenced yard and the three men entered the house.

They were in the livingroom of a fine, mid-Victorian brownstone house. Jackson's first impression was of the elegant spinet in one corner and the immense mohair couch facing the spacious fireplace with a bear rug in front of it. Then he became aware of the bookcase along the length of one wall, its shelves loaded with books, and of the oil paintings in heavy gold frames. Mrs. Curtis (Elaine, they learned for the first time), radiant and fascinating as ever, greeted both as old time friends.

"Dinner is served, gentlemen," she said gaily without further formality, and led the guests to the diningroom and their places.

Following the delightful dinner, they withdrew to the intriguing livingroom. Both Jackson and Gardner had half-heartedly offered to dry the dishes, and George, standing by, looked expectantly as though he hoped they would. But Elaine vetoed the idea.

"Land sakes," she protested, "I have nothing at all to do tomorrow, except to get George's meals and do those dishes. But we have too precious little time to talk with such men of affairs as the general manager and the chief photographer of the Hayden Survey. Now won't you men start 'talking shop' and not be too annoyed if I listen?'' She motioned them to seats; George proffered cigars and soon tongues were loosened.

As the evening wore on, numerous mutual friends and acquaintances were recollected; the affairs of the Land Office and of the Survey were thoroughly aired. George brought in maps from his study and they studied them minutely.

Jackson was taken aback somewhat when Elaine suddenly brought up the subject of the mountain with the snowy cross. When she reminded him that he must find and photograph that wonder of nature, he gaily promised to do his best, bolstering his own confidence by a silent reiteration that he'd find that mountain all right, for Emilie. When George offered to be on the lookout for any definite information that might lead the Survey party right to the mountain, he began to realize, even more than before, what a difficult task he had set for himself.

Oh, I come from Alabama
With my banjo on my knee,
And I'm goin' to Loo-sia-ana
My true love for to see.

The song that built the West rang out in the shrill
falsetto voice of Potato John on the clear morning air of
the twenty-fourth of May, as the Photographic Division
of the Hayden Survey headed northwesterly from Clear
Creek Camp. The usually taciturn major domo of the
commissary of the little party, mounted on Jerry, the

most dependable of the riding horses, led the cavalcade. Following close in column were the four grub mules, Girlie, Polly, Mag, and Peg, with Bill Whan riding Jed in whip position behind them. Next, came the aristocracy of the mules—Hypo and Gimlet—highly honored in that they bore the precious photographic equipment. Jim Cole followed, mounted on Jim, his namesake. Jackson on Jenny, Coulter on Jill, and Lt. Carpenter on Jack, with their summer's equipment compactly secured in saddle bags and rolls, were next in line, leaving Tom Cooper on Joe to bring up the rear.

Potato John set a fairly stiff walking pace for the animals and was in rare good mood. He seized upon the opportunity afforded by the gay atmosphere to run through his extensive repertoire of songs. Others felt moved to song, also, and joined in lustily as Potato John swung from one ballad to another.

Jackson chuckled inwardly as he visualized Potato John in the actual settings of his songs. The girl John left behind him; that money he bet on the bob-tailed nag; the railroad he had worked on; John dying for Annie Laurie; John tenting on the old camp ground (he really was a Union veteran); John dwelling in marble halls; John down in his old Kentucky home.

"Well, why not?" Jackson thought. "John might have been a gay young blade. The old boy really seems to have been around." And Jackson, too, joined in the singing, and for some time Emilie was with him in imagination, as Potato John called the settings.

A halt was called for rest after about an hour and a half with five miles covered. The going had been easy over the level ground in the Clear Creek bottoms. Jackson was following the bee-line suggested in Hayden's orders. They would skirt the foothills all the way to

Estes Park and make that destination by evening of the fourth day.

That evening saw the same jollity prevailing that had marked the daylight hours. The first night camp fire of any expedition served as a preview of what might be expected—in a social way—of its members. Potato John naturally took honors with his stories—all so preposterous that they evoked gales of laughter. Young Cole made an auspicious debut as the newly found vocalist of the group, demonstrating a truly good tenor voice.

"And I thought I could sing," Potato John moaned. "Now this young whippersnapper up and beats me all hollow. I ain't never goin' t' open my big mouth again with him in this gang."

"Until tomorrow," piped up Coulter, always ready to get John riled. "You know, John, I think I should tell Jim here how you got your name—Potato John."

Jackson sat by the fire, day-dreaming, hardly hearing Coulter tell the old familiar story.

"It's a western classic," began Coulter. "John was with the Survey in the Tetons two years ago, cooking a meal for the first time above timberline. He tossed the potatoes in the pot—and fifteen minutes after the water reached a rolling boil, I set up a howl for John to shake a leg with the potatoes. He moaned about how he 'couldn't figure out them damn spuds—never seed such gosh awmighty damned hard ones after all that cooking.' I couldn't resist, so I said 'John, what's got into you, putting stones in the pot instead of potatoes.'" A few snickers broke out around the campfire, and Potato John pretended not to be listening.

"So," continued Coulter, "I had to prove it—I reached into the pot and pulled out a hot potato. John here yelled and carried on, thought the skin would peel

49

right off my hand, didn't you, John? Well, anyhow, I gave John a lecture on the effects of altitudes on boiling points and all I ever got out of John was that he'd be damned. Ever since, he's been Potato John."

The next day found the little calvacade camping near Boulder, a bustling little town already designated as the site of the state university. Slower progress was made when a rain and hail storm in the Boulder foothills struck with such intense fury that Jackson's men could do little else than put their backs against the storm until it spent itself. Drying out was project number one for that afternoon and evening in camp.

The going and the weather were somewhat improved the following day, and the party camped for the night at Lyons.

Entering the St. Vrain Canyon the fourth day, they reached the lower end of Estes Park for the night camp. The following morning, they saw Estes Park for the first time, its lofty, towering Long's Peak in the distance.

That first day in the Park—May 28—was set aside for preparation for Jackson's first picture making of the season. About the first sight greeting their eyes that morning was a summer cottage which they noted was occupied—a strange circumstance for so early in the year. As if in answer to their unspoken query, a tall, lithe man in his early forties came down to the camp from the cottage to greet them.

"John Hubbell's my name, sir," he said, in unmistakable British accent, as he extended his hand to Jackson who had advanced to greet him. "We have recently arrived from Liverpool, having come on Lord Dunraven's invitation. It is my pleasure to welcome your party to the Park and to bear Mrs. Hubbell's request that you dine with us this evening."

50

"Why," Jackson replied, "that's very kind of you. Too kind, I'm afraid, when you realize that there are seven of us."

"Seven or seventy—it's no matter," Hubbell declared emphatically. "I assure you the pleasure will be all ours."

Further protestations were of no avail, and it was finally agreed that the seven wayfarers would descend upon the Hubbell home that evening. But, after he returned to the cottage, there were mumblings that indicated all were not as one in the matter of dinner that evening.

"Do you mean that me'n Tom and John have got to eat with them Britishers?" Bill Whan demanded.

"Yeah," broke in Cooper. "We'd look pretty eating with them high-toned folks."

"What's the matter, ain't my cookin' good enough?" petulantly inquired Potato John, trying to imply that his feelings were hurt.

"Why, you yellow-livered coyotes," snorted Coulter, "it's about time you learned how to act in nice company. You bet you're going to go, and like it, too."

"We'll tell you what to do," chimed in Carpenter soothingly, "when to bow, when to use a fork and all that stuff."

"Why not let Bill go up and tell them he has another engagement," Cole chimed in, "with this Estes fellow, if he feels that way about it."

"That's an idea!" Coulter laughed at the outlandish idea of the packer having a previous engagement.

"No," Jackson finally felt obliged to say, "Mr. Hubbell invited all of us and we accepted. He would be hurt if he thought any of us were troubled over attending the dinner. We're going—all of us."

51

And it was as simple as that—they went. Not, however, until after Lt. Carpenter, generally accepted as the social arbiter of the group, undertook to coach the "yellow-livered coyotes" in the intricacies of dining indoors at a table and with ladies present. His coaching went on through the entire afternoon. Promptly at six o'clock, seven men in varying degrees of trepidation — even though in their best available dinner clothes—appeared on the screen porch of the Hubbell cottage. If the host saw anything ludicrous in the appearance of his guests, he gave no indication as he greeted them.

"We are seven, also," he explained, ushering them inside and introducing them to Mrs. Hubbell and the five children—Goeffry, a striking young man of nineteen; Elizabeth, a comely lass of seventeen; Mary, plump and round of face at thirteen; and the irrepressible ten year old twins, David and Edward.

"Finest family I ever seen," Tom Cooper reported later. "Them pretty fillies and fine boys. And the old lady—I could go fer her myself." And that just about summed up the reaction of each of the visitors.

The "old lady," for all of her thirty-eight years, was indeed someone to go for. Short and plump as her husband was tall and slender, she effused geniality. The informality and genuine warm-heartedness of all the Hubbells immediately put the visitors at ease. Carpenter drew his first free breath since Hubbell's visit that morning as he sensed that his pupils in etiquette were hardly likely to let him down now.

Cole was enraptured with Elizabeth, but it was Potato John who was the life of the party, at least for the twins and Mary. The youngsters had never known such a wonderful man, such an amazing story teller. The boys resolved then and there that they were going to be mountaineers and grow up just like John. John was in his glory. At times, he was forced to grope for words to replace those which had always seemed apt to him, but in this particular setting didn't seem to be the right ones to use. In these lapses, Bill Whan and Tom Cooper came to his assistance, prompting with just the right expression.

The conversation at the other end of the table, if a little less lively, was fully as informative. The host had served for years in the British Foreign Office and had been stationed at posts in India, Burma, China and Japan. It was no small decision for Hubbell to make when invited by Lord Dunraven to give up a promising future with the Foreign Office to take up ranching in the little known American West. With the acquiescence of his family, he had made that decision and the future would determine if he had erred. He was certain he had not.

From Jackson, from Coulter, and from Carpenter, Hubbell and Goeffry learned of the work of the Hayden Survey. Before the evening came to a close they heard about the Oregon Trail, the great cattle trails, the building of railroads and pioneer settlements. No one could have done a better job of selling the West than did these three down-easterners who had done so much in popularizing the western region among their countrymen.

May 30 found the party still camped near the Hubbells. It was Lt. Carpenter who reminded Jackson of Memorial Day and suggested some sort of observance. Jackson readily approved the idea. Every member of the party, save Jim Cole, had seen service in the Union Army and some were already enrolled in the Grand Army of the Republic. Why shouldn't the little isolated group of veterans observe in their own way the day set aside a few years before by General Logan for honoring the comrades who had given their lives in the Great Rebellion?

And so it was that the Hubbells spent their first Memorial Day in their adopted country joining in the observance as guests of six men who looked back with justifiable pride on their years with the Army of the Potomac.

The program was simple but impressive. Jackson briefly explained the import of the day; all joined in singing the "Battle Hymn of the Republic"; Potato John strummed several appropriate selections on the guitar; and Jim gave a most creditable rendition of "Tenting Tonight." A moment of silent prayer in the awesome mountain setting terminated the first recorded Memorial Day observance in Estes Park.

The next morning found the party facing the stark reality of the work at hand. For the first time since leaving Clear Creek Camp, Jackson "made" some pictures, mostly of Long's Peak from different angles. Each entailed considerable climbing and setting up of the dark tent, making the exposures and doing the developing immediately.

Jackson's old "dark room on wheels" had long since been left to rot in the livery stable grounds in Omaha. In the field, he used in its stead a heavy, orange-colored tent and found it a most effective means of shutting out unwanted light. In making a photograph, it was first necessary to coat the glass plates with a syrupy mixture of collodion. This was allowed to become tacky and was then sensitized in a tray of nitrate of silver. Then the plate was placed in a plate holder and thence into the camera. After exposure, the plate was developed and allowed to dry. Then a light copal varnish was spread on the sensitized side for protection. The plate was then ready to use in making prints.

Most of the printing was allowed to await the winter months in Washington; the real arduous work of securing and carrying hundreds of plates of glass, of sensitizing them, of exposing and developing, took place in the field, often under most trying conditions.

During these first days of photographing in the Long's Peak region, Jackson was successful in completing a score or more of rare pictures, developing and cataloguing them and packing them securely, ready for shipment at the earliest opportunity to the safety of headquarters in Denver.

It ain't gonna rain, it ain't gonna snow,
It ain't gonna rain no mo';
Come on ev'ry body now
It ain't gonna rain no mo'.

When Gardner had given Jackson sketchy directions to guide the Photographic Division through the summer, he had included: "Work down the Snowy Range to Gray's . . ."

Work was really the name for it. Just as Jackson "made" rather than "took" his pictures, just so did the photographic party make its way through the mountains. Existing roads were followed whenever possible, which was by no means often enough. The larger share of the movement was over paths cut through scrub timber, over, under, or around fallen trees, through rocky canyons and mountain streams. They encountered working mines and abandoned mines, sawmills and lumber camps, live towns and ghost towns. More often they encountered virgin country, totally lacking any indications that man, white or red, had ever preceded them. From time to time, deer trails speeded up the progress and just as often beaver dams slowed them down.

The elements, too, played a hand in making life miserable for the little band. Weather in the Rockies, always unpredictable, was even more intensely so in those early June days in 1873. Snow, rain, hail with an occasional smile from the sun all were part of each day as the group trudged, hacked, and sloshed through the rugged Colorado terrain. There were days at a stretch when no photography could be accomplished and many in which but an hour or two of picture making appeared on the credit side of the work ledger.

Weather and the elements were not the only difficulties besetting Jackson and his men. Fellow humans frequently were guilty of making life less pleasant for them. Although most ranchers were friendly and hospitable, others, remembering long years of "proving up" on their claims, guarded their lands jealously and refused grazing or even tethering of pack or riding animals any where on their property. In some instances, after the party had come upon a particularly likely spot for camping, a hostile rancher would appear and peremptorily order them off. A Colt .45 strapped about his middle lent convincing emphasis to his demands. On such occasions, Jackson would say that his party was a government agency, and explain the work they were doing and that they were prepared to pay reasonable fees for using the land or for any damage the men or animals might do. Reactions to his calm persuasiveness were varied. Sometimes an angry rancher was mollified and relented. Some completely reversed their stands and offered Jackson "anything you want." Then there were those who didn't "give a damn who in hell you are" and who maintained they didn't "owe the government nothin'." And there were times when ranchers agreed to accept the "reasonable fee," only to charge such an outrageous sum as to make an army sutler's prices take on the semblance of give-away bargains.

Small parties of roving Ute Indians were encountered often; they, too, realizing Jackson had little authority over the land, issued edicts: "White man no camp here." And usually they had their way.

At times like these, Jackson's men would stand about with sullen but determined faces, a warning that they would allow an outsider to go just so far with their leader and no further. A nod from Jackson would have brought a Bill Whan or a Tom Cooper fist crashing against the jaw of the "enemy." But Jackson chose not to do business that way. He always insisted that he do the talking in any controversy; that he assume the entire responsibility. If he failed to win over recalcitrant ranchers through reason, he would never resort to threats or intimidations. He would move on to a camp site to which no one could raise objections though doing so might entail hours of back-breaking toil. His satisfaction lay in the thought that later the rancher might "see the light" and that other parties which chanced that way would benefit.

The loyalty showed by his men was an attribute of—a passion with—all members of the Hayden Survey. All had been chosen for their places on the team after careful scrutiny. Dr. Hayden possessed an uncanny ability to judge character correctly. He *knew* his men when he took them on and they never failed him. Mistakes they made, to be sure, errors of judgment, but never of intent. Not one of the hundreds who, over the years, worked under his direction ever proved disloyal in the slightest degree. Personal comforts and desires they subordinated to the all-absorbing work of the Survey. Further, they showed explicit confidence in the men the Doctor chose as division leaders and gave the same loyalty to them.

When the going was tough in Jackson's little branch of the Survey, if tempers grew a little ragged and an inclination arose to "chuck it all," someone would invariably come up with some expression of levity to ward off all semblance of grouching. A hearty laugh served always as an antidote for dissatisfaction. When a mule stumbled, by accident or design, flinging his load galley-west, necessitating complete repacking—to say nothing of replacing broken or lost items—Potato John could be sure to come up with "Ain't he the cutest thing? He's gettin' so's he can throw that stuff farther every time he flips."

Or when rain came down so hard and so long that men, animals, and equipment were soaked to the point of dissolving, Coulter could be depended on for: "Say, can you beat this Colorado sun for quick drying after a rain?"

A particularily heavy tree or a large boulder obstructing passage of the party was sure to bring forth from Tom Cooper, the only admitted agnostic of the group, a pious, impassioned, and imploring: "Oh, God, give me strength." The ensuing guffaws were sufficient to tone down griping for the rest of the day.

Bill and Tom and John did most of the cussing among the group of men who could, on occasion, prove themselves past masters in that art. The three experts knowingly or unknowingly were humorous even in their selective choice of epithets and invectives. Coulter, for diversification, was the most proficient perpetrator of practical jokes. Many of these were intended to give the cussing gentry practice in their chosen field, sometimes solely to see if the boys knew words over and above those they had been using. Cole, young and in love, couldn't remain downcast for any length of time; there was always the possibility of a letter from Elizabeth Hubbell when they hit the next town. He just didn't count, either in gripes or in hilarity. Lt. Carpenter, pretty much the philosopher of the group, usually managed to reason through any difficulty by means of logic. As for Jackson, his was the responsibility of leading the expedition through successfully, hence discouragement or defeatism on his part just could not be. He always thought of Emilie; for her he was going to find and photograph that strange mountain.

The men knew the present constant daily struggle would not continue indefinitely. They knew that Jackson planned the route and the itinerary with the canniness of a traffic manager. The larger the town, the greater its entertainment potentiality; thus it meant a stopover of longer duration. There would be supplies to purchase, overhauling of equipment to do, horses and mules to be shod, mail to be received and sent and fun to be had. To Jackson, the larger towns meant a greater certainty of receiving letters from Emilie and more authentic information on the surrounding country. To Coulter and Lt. Carpenter, a thriving city afforded the opportunity of contacting other scientists and comparing notes with them. To Whan and Cooper and Potato John, it meant relief from the hum-drum of "pounding trail" and a chance for a little "whoop-de-da."

Since leaving the delightful atmosphere of Estes Park, the minds of all had centered on the first big town on their route—Central City. The hardships they endured were made less hard in gay anticipation of that "wide open and up and coming mining town." And after that there would be Georgetown and Colorado Springs and Manitou and Fairplay. Let the winds howl; let the rains pour; let the arduous labors of the trail try men's souls . . . what the hell . . . all would be over and behind them when they hit Central.

Sundays invariably afforded respite from the labors of the week. Respite, but not necessarily rest. Generally, each man did what seemed expedient at the moment. If not in or near a town, the law of economic independence prevailed—freedom to do one's own washing, mending, and often preparation of food. Even Potato John was supposed to have a vacation from the skillet on the Sabbath. More often than otherwise, however, he performed the culinary tasks for all, preferring not to permit "You amatoors messin' with my cookin' stuff."

Whether John did the cooking or not, Sundays usually afforded the best eating of the week. Any group of men can claim one or more good hunters or wizards with hook and line. Jackson's party was composed of men who could hunt or fish with equal facility and loved nothing better. Lt. Carpenter had a little edge on the rest with a rifle and during the summer brought down more pheasants, wild turkeys, geese and ducks than any

62

of the others. Occasionally a deer was shot to lend variety to the sow-belly or the jerky—staples in Potato John's menus. Cole, young as he was, proved the best angler of the group, and many were the fish fries enjoyed by the men as a result of his skill. Both hunters and fishermen had ample time on Sundays to demonstrate their prowess.

The first ten days of travel along the Snowy Range were highlighted by stop-overs in the mining towns of Ward, Middle Boulder, and Caribou, welcome respite from the ordeals of the trail. Photographs were made of the towns, sometimes of townspeople and not infrequently of tourists who thought having their pictures taken outside of a gallery was a great novelty. But the main effort was devoted to pictures of outstanding peaks and features along the range—Long's Peak, Morraine Lake, Red Rock Lake, Brainerd Lake, James Peak, and many other streams and canyons.

Wherever the photographic apparatus was set up curious townspeople, ranchers and tourists watched with keen interest. After all, photography was a new art and more especially so in the western mountains. The onlookers watched with the eagerness of children anticipating some new joyous wonder and yet were careful not to impede the photographic men in their work. Generally, Jackson could set up his apparatus, make his exposures, even do the developing, scarcely aware that he was being observed by a host of interested spectators.

Securing topographical information was also a matter of conversation with the old timers, the people who knew the country. News-hungry natives were all too eager to swap talk with the Survey men and they, in turn, received many leads from their newly found friends. Miners, trappers, and an occasional Indian were not the least loathe to inform the picture maker of "hidden" lakes, "lost" mines, "secret" passes, or freaks of nature. Usually they accompanied their information with offers to guide the party directly to these mysteries.

None of these "tall tales" were ever put off lightly by Jackson. He was well aware that there were notorious liars in the mountain country and many folks gullible enough to believe everything they were told. But he was also cognizant of the fact that many hitherto unbelievable stories had been proven true to the everlasting chagrin of pompous and dogmatic persons who had pronounced the "humbugs" preposterous or impossible. He, himself, had done plenty with his photographs in the Yellowstone to humiliate such cocksure individuals. The wilder the tale he heard, the deeper study he made of it to ascertain its truth.

In the cramped lobby of the Mills Hotel in Ward one evening, the conversation got around to the mysteries of the West. Jackson and Carpenter and Coulter were among the loungers, swapping tales with the local gentry and visiting easterners.

"You've heard tell of the Snowy Cross?" offered Jed Coburn, a local miner, glorying in the role of "learnin' them softies a thing or two."

"Never heard of it," spoke up a Boston gentleman. "But, come to think of it, I've noticed lots of places astride these mountains where one could imagine crosses of snow, or elephants, or most anything for that matter."

"I mean *the* Snowy Cross," Jed insisted. "It's tarnation big and it's there all the time—never disappears." He spat into the spittoon and cocked an ear for the next query.

"Have you seen it?" Jackson inquired, trying to appear only mildly concerned.

"Wal, no. Can't say as I have," Jed admitted.

Gray's Peak and Torrey's Peak.

Chicago Lake, Mount Rosalie (now Mount Evans).

Garden of the Gods, Colorado Springs.

Gateway to the Garden of the Gods.

Cathedral Spires, Garden of the Gods.

Great Moraine on the Arkansas.

Panorama from summit of Mount Lincoln.

Ute Falls, Ute Pass.

"But I've known them as has," he added hastily.

"Anybody around here who has seen it?" queried the Bostoner, getting back into the conversation.

"Wal, yes, there's Captain Berthoud, Jim Baker, Jim Beckwourth, Uncle Dick Wooton and a lot o' other fellers. And lots o' Injuns has seed it." Jed smiled in confidence.

"Any of those people about—living here?" Jackson inquired, no longer restraining his eagerness. Here was an opportunity to get information on the very project he was most concerned with.

Jed's slow acknowledgment that "come to think of it, can't recall anybody here who's really seed it" didn't help any. And his further volunteering that "everybody knows about it" was exasperating. The Boston gentleman, in an effort to keep the conversation going, asked: "Where is this mountain, anyway?"

"Oh, off hand, I'd say nigh onto a hunnerd mile south o' here," Jed offered cautiously.

"Then that would put it around Canon City?" Jackson interposed. "Is it on this side of the divide?"

"Just can't exactly say," Jed faltered and was becoming just a little out of sorts since the conversation was getting out of his control. "All I know," he added, "there's a snowy cross down there someplace."

Well, at least, Jackson thought, people are talking about it. There must be something to it. Almost every time he talked with strangers anywhere along the route the matter came up. But, these chance conversations always ended with the same monotonous, "No, I haven't seen it myself, but I know it's there some place."

It would have been measurably less strenuous on Jackson and his men had they been able to by-pass the taller peaks instead of climbing them. They were not

65

out on this expedition, however, to make life easy. Rather, they were out for topographical information and to collect this knowledge in the form of pictures. The tall peaks were climbed—all of them—and the cumbersome equipment went along. The exposures made from all angles atop these vantage points, when pieced together, were to completely map this vast section abreast the Continental Divide. Jackson had to plan every exposure meticulously to give the American public a true conception of the vastness as well as the beauty of the great West.

The pattern of attack on each mountain was comparatively simple. As the party reached the base of a peak, camp was set up and the men, animals, and equipment to accompany Jackson on the particular climb were selected. An ascent was always attempted early in the morning. When the top was reached, the apparatus was set up and Jackson made such exposures as seemed expedient. If the day were clear and he was able to get in the work desired, the descent was made the same day. If, on the other hand, the going was tough and the weather bad, if the mules floundered in the drifts and made unpacking and repacking necessary, shelters were set up as conveniently as possible and the attempt deferred until the following day. Seldom, if ever, did they return to base camp until all desired pictures were made.

James Peak (through which the Moffat Tunnel has since been holed) was conquered in a one-day routine expedition by Jackson, Bill Whan, and Mag, who floundered and flipped but little. They were back at the base in time for a late supper. They had been fortunate in hitting upon a trail up through lofty Englemann spruce. It wound alongside torrential streams and crossed at points where a light skip and a hop was all that was required of a man and where a mule could be led through without slipping on rocks or icy slopes. Such drifts as had accumulated during the winter had deteriorated into patches of grayish crystalline, more coarsely pulverized ice than snow. Nature had supplied this trail negligently with rocks and boulders, always such physical and mental hazards for mules. The absence of fallen timber made the going much less difficult.

Conquering Arapaho Peak, on the other hand, took three days, due to bad weather and deep drifts. On that climb, Jackson had taken Tom Cooper and Peg and Polly had been selected for the job of bearing the burden of the heavy packs. This time no good trail could be found. When a likely looking way around a drift appeared, men and mules would scurry along expectantly only to encounter a series of jagged, slippery rocks. And all too often huge trees lay as a barrier. Wide, roaring streams strewn with giant boulders made crossing next to impossible. Men and animals struggled on none the less, ascending a little here, backtracking there, side-stepping, slipping, sliding and falling only to get up again to continue the ordeal. By sundown of the first day, they had been unable to reach the top of forbidding Arapaho Peak. Camp was pitched under protection of a toppled spruce tree. Jackson and Tom ate a cold meal glumly while Peg and Polly nibbled at such tufts of grass as they could find. Before noon of the next day, they managed to make the top and Jackson made several exposures. As always, these were developed on the spot and packed safely away in an *aparejo*.

The descent was every bit as arduous as the uphill climb and sundown overtook them before they reached base camp. So they pitched camp again and consumed all remaining food they carried with them.

The scientists of Jackson's party, who remained back at base camp and of necessity confined their search for specimens close by, were considerably perturbed when Jackson and Tom had not returned by the evening of the second day.

"Jack tells us not to worry," Coulter said, "until three days pass and they haven't returned. Nevertheless, I say we ought to start after them by tomorrow morning."

Carpenter and Cole agreed, and, early the next morning, set out in search of their friends. Fortunately their services as rescuers were not needed, for they had not ascended very far when they came upon the bedraggled men and mules heading for camp and rest. They had completed their mission successfully.

In this fashion, the Photographic Division *worked* down the Snowy Range, making pictures of anything and everything that could tend to complete the mosaic of the West.

Oh, what was your name in the States?
  Was it Thompson or Johnson or Bates?
Did you murder your wife and fly for your life?
  Say, what was your name in the States?

On the ninth of June, ten tortuous days after leaving the Long's Peak region, Jackson and his party reached the thriving, bustling, fabulous mining town of Central City. Morale was never higher as they moved up through Blackhawk, past Russell's Gulch, Gregory Lode, and on into Central City. The cavalcade of seven

69

men and thirteen animals caused almost no interest among the citizens who were very much accustomed to the sight of pack trains trudging to and from the surrounding mines. The men gaped and gawked as they moved through the town past the newly completed Teller House, the Montana Theatre, the St. James M.E. Church, and to the camp site west of the town arranged for by James Stevenson, Hayden's over-all superintendent of operations.

With an evening in town in prospect the men drew lots to see who would remain in camp as guard. Seven beans, six white and one black, were placed in a hat. This time, Lt. Carpenter "drew black" and, quite early in the afternoon, the rest headed for town.

Jackson, with Coulter for company, looked after business first. There was the matter of food for man and beast. John's traveling pantry was fairly well depleted and there would be little chance to stock up again until they hit Georgetown. H. J. Kruse's Grocery and Provision House was able to supply the staple groceries, as well as oats for the animals. In Tappan's Hardware and Stove Store they found articles needed for repairs to *aparejos* and harness.

Jackson was attracted by a sign in J. Collier's Photograph Gallery. Propped in the center window display of the proprietor's handicraft, the sign read:

"Work stood the test and came out on top in the largest city in Scotland. Now hanging in London to challenge the world."

"Hummm. Very interesting," Jackson remarked to Coulter, "believe I'll meet the gentleman."

"All right, Jack, go ahead," Coulter replied. "But count me out. I'll be waiting for you here." He pointed next door to "Chase And Sears, Tobacco and Seegars."

"I'll only be a minute or two," Jackson assured him.

As Jackson entered the shop a little man, unmistakably Scotch, red-faced with silver mixed in the red of his hair and sideburns, came from the rear room, lifted the hinged counter and faced Jackson expectantly, rubbing bony hands together.

"Yes, sir-r," he said, "could I ser-rve you?"

"My name is Jackson, Mr. Collier," Jackson introduced himself. He extended his hand and explained, "I'm in charge of the Photographic Division of the Hayden Survey."

"Aye," the Scotchman said, his eyes lighting in recognition of his visitor. "Jackson o' the Yellowstone. I hae heerd muckle o' you aboot and hae seen your-r-r pictures. I'm verrra happy t' ken you." He pumped Jackson's hand warmly.

"And I'm very glad to make your acquaintance. I was admiring your portraits, and I must confess I was somewhat intrigued by your notice in the window."

He motioned Jackson to one of the chairs, beaming at the compliment. "Aye, thank you. It's true, Mister-r-r Jackson. I had a studio in Glasga and war-r doin' quite well, if I do say so mysel'. The confinement caused me to develop a wracking cough. I heer-r-red o' the health giving qualities o' th' dry air herrre in Colorado and herrre I am."

"Do you go in for scenery at all?" Jackson asked.

"Nay," was the reply. "My trrraining and experrri-ence has been porrtraits and I'll stick t' them. Howeverrr, I do vastly admire your-r-r scenes."

At this point, Jackson mentioned that there was one scene he had his heart set on getting during the summer—The Snowy Cross.

71

"Aye," Collier agreed. "This cross should be pic-turrred. 'Tis a wonderrful work o' th' Creator-r-r."

No, he had not seen it, he told his visitor, even though he had covered on foot or horseback almost every foot of ground within a radius of some seventy-five miles from Central.

"But," he went on, "I saw a mon just t'other-r-r day who claimed he hae seen it frae a spot on what he called Tennessee Pass, down near-r-r the new mining camp o' Oro."

Now Jackson was really interested. He plied Collier further but could learn only that the "mon was frae Fairrrplay, a miner-r-r by the name o' Smith."

Jackson hoped he could find the miner by the name of Smith when he reached Fairplay and told Collier he would make every effort to do so. This might be a real lead.

Collier expressed a desire to observe Jackson at "worrrk" and Jackson, very pleased, suggested the second day following. To this Collier readily assented.

"I'd like you t' see my shop, too, Mister-r-r Jackson," Collier invited.

Jackson followed him through the "draw bridge" counter and into the "sitting room." Actually the room offered nothing unusual. There were the many screens used for light adjustment, the skylight, an assortment of cameras, and a stool with an iron "head holder." But Collier was so obviously proud of his equipment Jackson felt compelled to be laudatory of them.

Jackson suddenly remembered that Coulter was waiting for him, undoubtedly out of patience by this time. Following mutual expressions at the pleasure of meeting, he left quickly with Collier's " 'til day after to-morrrra" ringing in his ears. He found Coulter leaning

72

against the window of the tobacco shop, puffing on one of the "home rolled seegars" and listening to a piano in Moran's Saloon. The player could not be seen, even when the doors swung wide, but his patter filled the street as he swung from tune to tune. As Jackson appeared, Coulter motioned to him to listen.

"Say, he is good," Jackson admitted. "Wonder who he is?"

"Well, there's a way of finding out," Coulter said, leading the way across the street.

The two entered the saloon. The smoke within was so dense they could see little but the large, suspended and swinging coal oil lamps until their eyes became accustomed to the haze. Then, at the far end of the room they saw a small stage and before it the lone piano. The player was a thin, haggard, sickly looking man of doubtful age. Jackson eyed the sorry looking figure intently.

"That fellow looks familiar," he confided to Coulter. "Let me figure him out."

They took seats at one of the very few unoccupied tables, where they could observe the piano player closely. Ordering their drinks, they settled down to watch the man fingering the keys, rendering selection after selection, mostly of the sadly sentimental kind. As he turned in the direction of Jackson and Coulter, his face seemed to light up momentarily with a faint glow of recognition—but only momentarily. He dropped his gaze and resumed playing.

As Jackson sat staring intently at the sorry looking player, thinking of possible places where he might have encountered him, Coulter broke in.

"Well," he said, "I could think of many things more thrilling than trying to guess the identity of a tramp ivory tickler."

Jackson realized his friend was getting slightly bored with the evening's developments, so he rose from the table and approached the stranger.

"Pardon me, my friend," he said, looking searchingly into the man's face, "but I believe we've met. Can you enlighten me?"

Without raising his eyes from the keys, but with a rather cold and unfriendly shrug, the piano player said: "Think hard, Bill. You ought to remember."

At the mention of his name, Jackson jerked his head sharply and stared more intently into the face of this strange man. Very few people called him Bill—at least since army days—so this fellow must be some boyhood or army friend. The darn fool, Jackson thought, doesn't want me to recognize him, even though he let on he does know me. Slowly the piano player raised his eyes to Jackson and stared back.

"My God!" the player exclaimed, his eyes switching back to the piano keys. "I didn't know I had changed that much."

He finished the sad strains of "Darling Nellie Gray," paused and looked up at Jackson.

"Remember Gettysburg, Bill? Before you got hoity-toity and went on special duty as regimental artist?"

That did it! Instantly, Jackson saw before him an old army comrade—a squad mate, a bold, fine looking, bright-eyed, happy-go-lucky companion of many an escapade during the war days.

"Ned Beardsley, you old sinner!" Jackson blurted out, grasping the man by his shoulders and shaking him. "What in hell are you doing out here? Haven't seen or heard of you since old Colonel Blunt put me on that detail."

A mirthless smile played over Ned's face. "Oh, rat-

74

tling the ivories, as you can see. Don't you like my playing?''

"Quit stalling, Ned,'' Jackson demanded, shaking his shoulders more forcefully. "Out with it. What have you been doing?''

"You mean, how did I sink so low? If you don't mind, Bill, I'd rather not talk about it.'' He fumbled through the sheets of music.

"But you must, Ned. If you're in trouble, I'm the one to help you.''

"I'm not in trouble. I'm just a bum and nothing can be done about it. Bill, I-I . . . I've been a plain damn fool. I-I'm no good. It's this stuff,'' he swept the room with a wave of his hand, "that caused it. I've made my bed and I'll lie on it.'' He turned back to the piano as if the matter were closed.

"Hey, whats wrong wizh zhat mushic box?'' shouted a drunken miner with a party girl perched on his knee. "Give uush shom muzhic!''

"Yeah,'' prompted the girl. "You broken down ivory rattler; you haven't earned your supper yet.''

"You see, Bill,'' Ned said, resuming his playing. "I'm kicked around by the likes of these. And I'll just have to go on.''

"Like blazes you will! You're coming with me. We'll work something out.''

"Going to stay here all night,'' Coulter broke in. "It's about time to be on our way.''

"Just a minute, Coulter,'' Jackson replied. "Be with you just as soon as I get this stubborn critter to come with us. Coming, Ned?''

Ned continued playing, his head dropped. Jackson and Coulter stood there in awkward silence, now quite aware of the dirty glances being cast in their direction

75

from all about the room. Suddenly, Ned stopped playing and banged the piano cover shut.

Rising from his stool he demanded, "Where to?"

"Just come along," Jackson said reassuringly. "Now you're showing some sense."

Over a good meal Ned unfolded his story bit by bit. It was the age old one of the down and outer—youthful ambition, the first flushes of success, easy-come-easy-go, the gaming table, drink, women, loss of money and friends, weakening health, the struggle to hold on and finally hand-to-mouth existence. He concealed nothing in his story, blaming no one but himself.

"And that's it, Bill," he concluded resignedly. "How can you find any salvage in an old wreck like me?"

"Ned, you're alive," Jackson countered. "You've retained your faculties. You were a sutler's helper in the army, I remember, and a darn good one. You can give a good account of yourself looking after property. We can get you started again and you'll be on your feet in no time."

"Who'd hire me—me with dissipation stamped all over and with my lungs shot?" His voice held disgust, not pity, for himself.

"We're going to help you, Ned," Jackson assured him. "You're going to join the Survey—without pay, mind you—until Dr. Hayden can put you on in some regular capacity. Meanwhile, you'll eat regularly, and help out where you can build up those lungs with good fresh Colorado air."

For a moment, the man's sunken eyes filled with tears, then he shrugged his thin shoulders and managed a weak smile. "Bill, you're so confident. I'm beginning to absorb some of your confidence. I-I-I'll just do my best. You're the boss, and I'll not let you down."

"None of that boss stuff, Ned," Jackson retorted.

"Just the same, Bill, you *are* taking charge. Don't let me get picked up as a vag and be farmed out to Moran again to work off a fine."

"We certainly won't," Jackson assured him. "You're staying here in the hotel tonight. Tomorrow, you're going out to camp and meet the boys."

Jim Cole entered the dining room and joined them.

"Say," Jackson said, "what about the other boys? Has anyone seen them?"

"I saw them two or three hours ago," Jim informed them, "going into the Montana Theatre. That show should be over any minute now. Let's round them up to go back with us. *They* might be tempted by the burlesque girls."

They lounged in front of the theatre until the doors opened. John, Bill, and Tom Cooper were about the last to emerge. They were not too happy to see their fellow Survey men, for they knew they were in for some heavy joshing.

Coulter called, "Good gosh, we thought you fellows would never come. Belle and Ella and Blanche sure got a grip on you, didn't they?"

"W-a-l-l," Tom Cooper drawled, "I bet we had more fun than you fellers did. Where yu' been, at a church sociable or somethin'? We seen our show and you done what you wanted to do, so what's the harm?"

"Who said anything about harm?" Coulter laughed. "We were just worried that these vampires," he pointed to the voluptuous girls displayed on the theatre billboard, "might have you in their clutches."

"They shore did," broke in Bill Whan. "When them tight-wearin' gals come down the aisle and one of them planked a smacker on John's forehead, the old boy nearly swooned."

"Oh, ho!" Coulter gloated. "Look at the lip-prints on his forehead."

"Aw, you're just jealous," Potato John growled, as they headed up the canyon street toward camp.

Go 'long mule, don't you roll dem eyes,
  You can change a fool,
But a doggone mule,
  Is a mule until he dies.

Sundays with the party were usually days when the men had time on their hands. This Sunday—June 12, 1873—was to be no exception, save for the admonition from Jackson that everything must be in readiness for an early departure the next day—they had to make Fairplay by July 7. He dispensed with the usual drawing for the black bean by announcing he would be in camp all day and would do any guard duty necessary. He spent his time reading, sketching, and in writing the daily edition of letters to Emilie.

Quite early the following morning, Jackson began to fear they would *never* make Fairplay. The express agent in Central refused to accept his checks in payment for new supplies sent up from Denver. Jackson ruefully contemplated a lost day awaiting confirmation of the checks from the bank in Denver. As he argued with the agent, the express office door opened and a round-bellied, bandy-legged man, swinging a heavy gold-headed cane, ambled in.

"And whut's wrong, young feller," he inquired, turning to Jackson. "Broke?"

Jackson, at first inclined to object to this stranger's interest in his own personal affairs, was about to retort sharply when he noted the kindly glint in the old gentleman's eyes. "Well, hardly that, sir," he said. "But the agent here says he can't accept checks, and I do not have sufficient cash to get a release on my supplies from Denver."

"Well now, maybe *I* kin help yez. How much yez need?" He flipped his cane over the crook of his left arm and dug deep into his right pants pocket.

"Seventy-five dollars is the amount of the check," Jackson replied hesitantly, wondering the while what kind of a discount would be asked.

"Jist sivinty-five dollars?" asked the man, incredulous that anyone would haggle over so small an amount. "Godawmighty!" He faced the agent and bellowed, "Zeke, giv this feller his stuff—I'll pay the charges."

"Just as you say, Pat," the agent agreed meekly. "But I'm warnin' you. You may get stuck with that check." Resignedly, he turned to lift the heavy packages of supplies up over the counter.

"Me name's Casey—Pat Casey," the man explained, holding out a fistful of money. "Whiniver I see a honest man in trouble—I help him."

Pat Casey! Jackson had often heard of the fabulously rich miner and the many stories going the rounds about how illiterate he was. This, then, was the man who had called down the mine shaft to his men, "How many o' yez are down there?" "Five," was the answer. "Well, half of yez come up and t' other half stay down."

And now the great man had turned up as his rescuer.

Jackson recovered from his stupefaction in time to blurt out his thanks and genuine pleasure at meeting Casey.

"I'm glad to know you, Mr. Casey," he said. "Thank you from the bottom of my heart for your kindness. I'm William H. Jackson of the Photographic Division of the Hayden Survey, and this is my packer, Tom Cooper. We've been in Central a few days and had hoped to move on today."

"Th' pitcher maker! Oh, me boy, it's right glad I am to know yez. My, how I'd like t' jine yer party." Pat's eyes glistened at the prospect.

"You're welcome to come along with us, Mr. Casey. You already have a seventy-five dollar investment with us, you know." Jackson offered this invitation as he accepted the $75 from Pat's open palm and placed thereon the check he had been trying to cash.

Keen disappointment spread over Pat's face. "Investment?" he fumed. "Who made an investment."

"Well, maybe not an investment, Mr. Casey," Jackson explained, sensing that he had said the wrong thing. "But you did put up $75 to cover that government check

81

in your hand. I've endorsed it over to you and you can get the money at your bank."

"I niver bother wid thim things," Pat stated emphatically and pushed the check back into Jackson's hands.

Jackson was at an absolute loss both as to words or acts to fit the situation. He stood stupified as Pat added: "And besides, I didn't put up $75. I give it to yez."

This was something new to Jackson; he couldn't bring himself to be an intermediary for the receipt of a gift to the government; nonetheless, he couldn't afford to offend this affable man. He made one more attempt to settle the matter in a business-like way.

"Mr. Casey," he said, "you are indeed very kind and I thank you warmly. I'll report your kindness, and later you will receive official acknowledgment."

But Pat would have none of that sort of business. He pulled himself up proudly, to his full five feet seven, settled his cane more firmly in the crook of his arm and looked Jackson square in the eye.

"Young man," the words came coldly and firmly, "I giv yez that money, and I don't want to hear no more about it."

Jackson squirmed, still feeling some sort of protest was in order, but quickly decided to yield. "Thanks, Mr. Casey," he said feebly. "This is most kind of you." He put the check back in his pocket and extended his hand to the blustery old man.

"And whin are yez lavin'?" Pat asked, sufficiently mollified now that he could turn his interest to something besides money.

"Just as soon as we can get to camp and be on our way. Do you think you could arrange to come with us on such short notice?"

"Well now, that's nice an' invitin'. I'll see if I kin make it."

Never dreaming that Pat would ever be on hand to accompany the party, Jackson bade him farewell and good fortune and hastened back to camp with Tom and the supplies. These new supplies made for some extra packing and heavier loads for the six pack mules, but the little caravan got under way in remarkably short time.

As it moved out, Jackson rode on ahead and alone into Central to transact some final business. He had all but forgotten Pat Casey in the final rush, but when he caught up with the pack train, there he was plodding along with the rest. He was mounted on a large bay horse, more of a draft animal than a saddle horse. Bulging saddle bags and a huge blanket roll clearly indicated that Pat had made up his mind in a hurry that he "cud make it" and intended to be with the party for some time. Casey had lost no time in packing for the trip; he was ready and waiting with his big bay, Mike, and a spare pinto when the caravan headed out of town and down the steep Virginia Canyon. Tom Cooper had, of course, recognized the genial Irishman, introduced him around, and invited him to fall in line. Pat had spotted Ned walking. There were but seven mounts for the eight men and Ned spurned offers of the others to "ride my nag a while."

"Kin yez ride, lad?" the kindly old miner had inquired of Ned and had received a reply in the affirmative. "This here mare is kinda wild," Pat warned, apparently explaining why he wasn't riding her himself.

"Well," Ned had replied, lithely vaulting into the saddle, "she can't do more than pitch me to kingdom come."

The man who a few short nights before had seemed likely game for some undertaker was literally a new man. Accepted friend as he was of every man in the party, none had the remotest idea of what he would or could do with a horse. For a few brief moments, the mare reared and bucked with Ned sitting the saddle as though welded to it. With an apparent realization that "this fellow can ride," the mare almost immediately became as docile as Gimlet when that cantankerous mule condescended to be on his extra good behavior. If Ned needed anything further to put him in solid with all, he was made by that one act of handling a "bucker." Jackson was more than proud of his old friend when the story of his horsemanship was related to him.

The route followed the Virginia Canyon road. It was so steep it offered physical hazards even for men who were walking. Riding animals often lost their footing on the descent with most disastrous results. Vehicles, when such came that way, had to be let down on the steeper slopes by means of strong ropes lashed to sturdy trees. Fortunately, Jackson's party, through using due caution, negotiated the descent without untoward incident. A few miles of that sort of nerve-wracking riding and the first likely spot for a camp was the first one chosen. It happened to be the bottom of a ravine, peaceful and surprisingly verdant, considering the heavy masses of snow still lying in drifts nearby.

In spite of the prevalent fatigue, Jackson, Pat Casey, and Bill Whan made their way to the very foot of Crater Peak, searching for the best route to be followed on the morrow when the full ascent would be made in earnest. In this trial run, they encountered immense bodies of deep-lying snow. The reconnaissance late that day proved valuable to Jackson, Bill, and Mag on the following one, for they were able to avoid treacherous drifts and make the climb, secure a few exposures, and return in the sunlight hours of one day.

For a few days the party struggled on without benefit of roads. To add to the difficulties, the beautiful weather they had enjoyed in Central became but a lingering memory as wind, hail, rain, and snow plagued them. In spite of the elements, Jackson managed to secure the photographs he desired and to adhere pretty close to his schedule.

They stopped only briefly at the mining towns of Mill City and Empire. Remembering that Gardner had warned that the "toll gate men at Georgetown are robbers," Jackson chose to use the seldom used trails up from Empire rather than the toll road. The choice proved a bad one. The worst travel yet experienced marked the struggle up that trail. The pack mules became stubborn, flipping loads right and left, floundering so frequently that Tom Cooper felt compelled to expostulate: "Them damn mules just love that deep snow. They actually hunt for the biggest holes just so they can laugh while we pull 'em out."

Tom was right in his appraisal of the intellects of mules. Those unpredictable animals really staged a mulish version of a wild party when the outer fringes of Georgetown were finally reached. Finding themselves suddenly on hard, dry, if dusty, streets after all that floundering in drifts or in mud, the pack mules let loose. Tom and Bill had been delegated the task of bringing up the heavily laden mules; the other men had ridden on ahead to establish the camp site. The two packers were more engrossed in Georgetown than in their charges. Suddenly, as if on signal from Hypo, who happened to be in the lead, the mules broke from their single column formation. Before Tom or Bill knew what was happening, the six mules were every where but on the street they had just been plodding along. Onto wooden-planked sidewalks, into yards, up alleys they clattered, loads and all, with Bill and Tom too amazed to give quick or effective pursuit. As the two men routed one mule from a yard, the other mules bolted into other yards wherever the gates were open.

After several futile attempts to corral their charges, Tom and Bill stopped to make an estimate of the situation. Bill, the more philosophical of the two, was the first to arrive at a plan of action. "Tom," he said, "them sons o' Satan is makin' monkeys out o' us. T' hell with 'em. Let's just wait for 'em to come out o' hidin'."

"But," interposed Tom, "what will them cantankerous, stubborn, cunnin', sweet little offsprings of horse fathers do while we're waitin'?"

"I don't give one sweet damn what they do!" Bill answered. "I'm plumb tuckered and ain't chasin' no more. I'm in favor o' corrallin' 'em one at a time, as they show up."

"Wal, I guess that's about as good a idee as any," Tom agreed. He plopped himself on the sidewalk and pulled Bill down beside him. The two sat glumly, awaiting developments.

Things were not long in happening. From the Metropolitan Livery Stable, just a few doors from where they sat, an angry man emerged, leading a chastened Mag and demanding in no uncertain tones, "Who in tarnation owns this confounded critter? Just let me lay my hands on him!"

"Start layin'," retorted Tom. "That mule broke loose from our train and we been huntin' fer her."

The angry townsman rudely thrust Mag's halter rope

into Tom's hands and snorted, "A fine thing—pack mules runnin' loose and trespassin' on a law abidin' man's property. I ought to have the law on you." He glared at Tom and Bill.

"Listen you," Tom said, "I ain't in no mood for arguin'. This here mule's ourn an' we're takin' her. If she has done any harm, Mr. Jackson will look after it."

"And just who's Mr. Jackson?" the man demanded.

"He's the boss o' our party, that's who—boss o' the picher-makin' part o' the Hayden Survey."

"You don't say?" the man exclaimed with a look of incredulity. "Well, that's different. The critter just tipped over a bar'l of oats and took a hefty kick at me is all. Take her, and good riddance. Say, what's that?" he asked, startled at what he saw up the street.

Out the open door of the printing office of the *Colorado Miner* came Hypo, followed closely by an aproned printer who was belaboring the mule with a broom.

Bill rushed up in time to rescue Hypo, and to try his hand at placating the irate printer. When he learned the mule belonged to the Survey, he quickly forgot his anger, and plied Bill with questions about Jackson and his party.

The friendly conversation was ended abruptly as a gang of youngsters came tearing down the street driving two scared mules, Girlie and Polly, before them.

"These your mules, mister?" one freckle faced youngster demanded of Bill. The packer gathered the halter ropes of the two erring mules and nodded.

"Well, mister," the freckled one continued, "you're sure in for it. They knocked down Mr. Wolcott's fence and trampled his garden. Gee, but he's mad."

"I don't blame him," Bill said resignedly. "But we'll pay him for any damage."

87

Tom, leading Mag, joined Bill who now had Hypo, Girlie and Polly in tow. Just at that moment, Mr. Wolcott caught up with the rapidly growing crowd, but before Wolcott, fuming and sputtering, could utter a word, Bill cut him off.

"Mister, if you think you got somethin' to whine about, look at me'n Tom. Mr. Jackson'll pay you, but he'll likely kill us."

Mention of Jackson again had that soothing effect the packers had observed before. Wolcott's anger melted.

"Jackson? Jackson, you say?" he panted. "Jackson of the Hayden Survey?" Bill nodded and Wolcott went on, "Why didn't you say so in the first place? Why, I've known Jackson ever since I've been in the West. No one could pick a fight with him, he's too fair and square. Where is he now?"

"He and th' others went up this here street half hour or so ago to pick out a campsite. Me'n Tom was s'posed t' follow," Bill informed him.

"Well, what are we waiting for?" Wolcott demanded, and turned to the crowd. "Come on, some of you fellows, let's help these men get to their camp."

"That's right nice of you," Bill said, "but we're still two mules short."

"No you ain't," shouted a man on the outer fringe of the tight packed circle. "Here are your critters." The crowd made way to allow him to lead in Gimlet and Peg.

Tom reached for the ropes of these last two wayward mules as the stranger continued: "This'n," he said, patting Gimlet lightly on the rump, "raised hob in Charley Forbes' Drug Store. Busted some medicine bottles, but that's about all. Stuck his snout in a barrel o' moth balls and let out a hee-haw that scared a passel o' women nigh t' death. When I grabbed his rope, he cum along as peaceful as a lamb. And this'n," he stroked Peg's neck, "ran out'n Widder Murphey's yard to line up with t'other as I cum this away."

Wolcott by now had assumed complete control. "Good work, Joe," he said, then raised his voice for the benefit of the crowd. "Just tell everybody any damage will be taken care of. These boys are with the government. You've all heard of Jackson, the photographer. He's their boss."

Bill thanked him and asked if it were all right to lead the mules on into camp.

"Sure, sure," came cries of assent from throughout the crowd. "Come on, open up. Let 'em on."

And Bill and Tom, now more or less triumphant, led the mules up the street, with the crowd following.

Part way, they met Carpenter and Coulter coming to learn what had happened to the pack train. They wheeled about and from there on led the impromptu parade to camp.

There was no triumph depicted on the faces of Bill Whan and Tom Cooper, however, as they tied the mules to the picket line and went about unpacking.

"Where in this great free nation of ours," Jackson began calmly enough, "have you been?"

"Now, Mr. Jackson," Bill began for the defense, "it was this a-way. We was a-comin' up the street when all of a sudden—"

"The goldanged mules bolted every which way," broke in Tom, realizing that he, too, had to assume some of the responsibility.

Continuing their unpacking, they proceeded to relate the whole sorry story.

"And the worst of it is," Bill concluded, "is that

you are going to have to pay a lot o' damages. Some feller named Allcloth, or something like that, is coming to see about it.''

"Will Jackson," came a voice from behind Jackson. It was Wolcott who had followed along to greet his old friend and to take possible wrath off the shoulders of Bill and Tom. "Welcome to Georgetown.''

"Well, I'll be—Wolcott!'' Jackson greeted the puffing and perspiring man. "Or should I say, Allcloth? Tom and Bill told me a man named Allcloth was coming up to collect damages.''

"I guess they meant me, all right,'' Wolcott laughed. "But, Will, you know me better than to think I came to collect for anything. I came to speak for your packers. They did all they could to stop the rampage.''

Jackson had previously made up his mind to release the packers from any further blame, but he had not reckoned with Pat Casey. He heard Wolcott's defense, broke into the discussion and offered to "take care of it all.''

Jackson, with a remark that "we'll take care of that tomorrow,'' shifted the conversation from the mules to reminiscing with Wolcott.

In time he managed to get Wolcott aside to ask him quietly to secure and submit to him all statements for damages committed by the Survey mules. He begged him, above all, to keep the details away from Pat Casey. Wolcott laughed heartily at the story of the $75 "gift'' in Central City.

"That's Pat all over,'' he said. "And if you value his friendship, don't ever try to repay that money. You'll hurt his feelings. And, Will, just leave the mule damage to me.''

Wolcott was out early the following day. True bar-

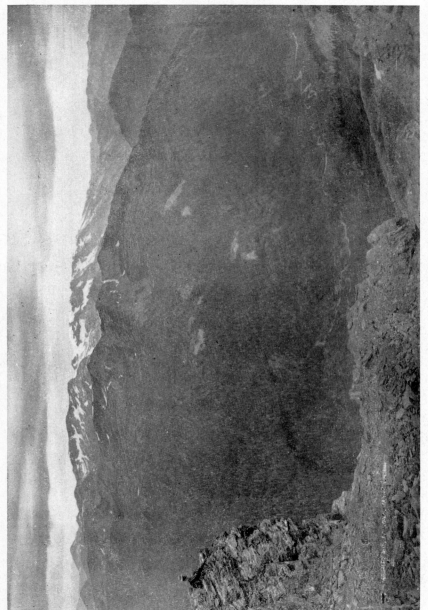

Treasure Mountain.

The Sawatch Range.

pened to remember, I ain't got these things in Georgetown, and it'll take a little time to get 'em here. How
long you going to be about?"

"We're due to be moving out over Griffith Mountain quite early tomorrow morning," Coulter answered.

"Well, that's too bad," Gassy said sadly, and shook
his head. "Can't possibly get 'em up here by then." To
all appearances, the deal was off. Not for Coulter, however. He wanted those specimens, and in pleading tones
he asked if it were not possible to ship the boxes to
Denver.

Gassy pondered for some time and finally said in
that confidential manner of his, "You know I'm going
to *give* you those things, for the government. But," and
Gassy really looked pained that he had to make this an-
nouncement, "I can't afford to pay the shipping charges
too."

"The costs wouldn't be too heavy," Coulter volunteered. "I think we could raise the money. How much
do you think they'd be?"

Gassy went through the motions of figuring and
came up with "Oh, somewhere around fifty dollars. The
worst of it is those pack train fellows want their money
in advance. They haul as far as Floyd Hill and then
transfer the freight to the Colorado Central Railroad,
you know."

Coulter was all for advancing the money to Gassy
at once, but he didn't have that much. He could get the
difference from Jackson as soon as he arrived. Would
Mr. Thompson remain for the evening meal?

The invitation left Gassy cold, but he was careful
not to show it. Unfortunately, he explained, his mining
interests in Empire prevented his accepting the kind
offer. But as to the shipment of the specimens—how

97

much could Coulter raise, now, so as not to miss out on this golden opportunity? When Coulter apologetically told him that thirty dollars was the limit of his cash, Gassy agreed to accept that, saying "I can trust you to send me the rest after you get back to Denver."

They parted with the best of well wishes, Coulter feeling he had made the best deal in his life, and Gassy cussing the luck that a measly thirty dollars was all he could claim for the day's work.

The world toppled down on Coulter when, at supper, he related the wonderful good fortune which had befallen him.

"Thompson? Gassy Thompson?" Pat Casey cried out. "If that skonk cud make tin dollars by tellin' th' trooth aginst five for lyin', he'd take th' five." He proceeded to tell all he knew of the notorious crook.

Later, Wolcott added fuel to the fire by stating that Gassy would ship something to Denver, all right, "just so's the law can't catch up with him. That scoundrel has an uncanny way of staying just within the law. He'll never sign any sort of agreement which could later be used as evidence against him."

"Well, I'm goin' t' get 'im if it's th' last thing I do," Pat said to Coulter. "Don't worry, me boy. I'll git that thurty dollars back an' more. And you take it now. Yer goin' an' I'll be stayin' t' look after that skonk." To the protesting Coulter, Pat turned a deaf ear. Down into that cavernous money bag he delved again and thrust three ten-dollar gold pieces into Coulter's pocket.

Jackson was most pleasantly surprised one day when, among letters from Emilie, he came upon one in a different hand, postmarked from Omaha. He quickly slit the envelope open with his pen knife and glanced at the signature. From Tim and Mary, his old friends in

98

Omaha! He read with increasing excitement:

Mr. William H. Jackson, Esquire,
Hayden Survey U.S.G.S.,
Care of Ford House,
Denver, Colorado Territory.
Dear Mr. Jackson:

Timothy asked me to write you to tell you about a man he met in the U.P. yards yesterday. This man was a tramp. He said he had been all over the West and that he had seen that strange mountain you told us about and said you were going to find if you could. He said this mountain was in about the middle of Colorado Territory. He said he saw it from another mountain. He cannot remember the name of this other mountain but he said it was about 25 miles north and west of a town called Alma.

We hope this will help you find it if you have not already. We hope you will bring us a picture of it , when you get back to Omaha.

The twins are fine and so is Tim. So am I. We pray God's blessing on you every day.

Your loving friends,
Tim and Mary.

This was the most concrete location he had gotten yet. You bet Tim and Mary would get a photograph of the strange mountain—framed!

That evening he mentioned the letter to Wolcott and added, "I've been intending to ask you: have you seen the Snowy Cross?"

"No," was the answer, "but everybody—"

"Knows of its existence," broke in Jackson. "Ed, I've heard that ever since we left Denver. Has anyone ever seen anyone who *has* seen the mountain?"

"Yes, by God, I have," Wolcott answered. "Just the other day I wrote a piece in which I mentioned the mountain and a friend who told me of it. Let's go over to the office and hunt up that copy."

They left the Barton House and went to the *Miner* office where Wolcott thumbed through back issues until he came upon his "piece" in the copy of June 16.

> We have an old and trusted friend who has pros-
> pected for years on the Range, who says that the very
> sight of the Mount of the Holy Cross, lying a hundred
> miles south of us, seems like a comforter to him and an
> old companion. There it stands, reaching to the heavens,
> visible from every mountain peak, a reminder of His
> love and watchfulness.

For a moment, Jackson was stunned. Only a hundred miles away! Right on their route! And visible from
every mountain peak! And all the time he'd been afraid
he'd never find it. Why hadn't he thought to ask Wolcott before?

"Is that its name—Mount of the Holy Cross?" he
asked.

"The only one I've ever heard," Wolcott replied.
"And you know, Will, the more I think of it, the more I'm
forced to the conclusion your Irish friends are right.
I'll try to get more information and send it to you. Meanwhile, I'd suggest that you inquire from every miner you
meet, especially those around Fairplay and the little
camp called Alma."

The route from Georgetown was over a trail on
Griffith Mountain toward Chicago Lakes. The climb
was comparatively easy and was very much enlivened by
a chance meeting with some of Wheeler's men coming
down over the Divide. They halted for a visit, checking
on mutual experiences and exchanging jibes. It was good
to learn that both parties were well along on summer
schedules, mapping the illimitable West.

Progress toward the Pike's Peak region was considerably faster than the slow pace marking their back-bend-
ing efforts in the Clear Creek Canyon. In beautiful South
Park, they were able to travel on roads for considerable
distances. Snow drifts were replaced by hot sands; wood

100

ticks and predatory animals gave way to ants and mosquitoes.

They encountered more people, more sod shanties. In South Park, especially, in whatever direction they looked they could see innumerable cattle and cultivated fields, with here and there rail fences around a rancher's claim.

Jackson had expected to meet Stevenson, the business manager of the Survey, when his party reached the Platte River. Stevenson had promised to be at a predetermined point with supplies and further instructions. When Stevenson did not appear, Jackson, with Bill Whan, rode over to Acequia Station on the new line of the Denver and Rio Grande Railroad and took the short train ride into Denver. Bill took both horses back to camp with instructions to meet Jackson at Acequia on the return train at noon the following day.

The twenty mile ride on the narrow gauge road afforded Jackson a welcome respite from pounding the trail, if only for a couple of hours. When he reached Denver, he made his way up F Street toward the Ford House, and met Stevenson leisurely proceeding down the teeming thoroughfare.

Stevenson immediately burst into an apology. "Jack," he said, placing his hands heavily on Jackson's shoulders, "I'll swear that up to this moment I have completely forgotten I was to meet you. Believe me I am sorry. What a business agent I turned out to be."

He looked so deeply humble that Jackson swallowed the sharp admonishment he had intended giving him. "All right, Steve," he answered with what amiability he could muster, "you're forgiven." After a momentary but awkward pause, he added, "But, Steve, I really didn't drop work for an afternoon just to come down here for an apology. What are the momentous issues we are to decide?''

Stevenson laughed, ''You win, Jack. But let's get out of the way of progress out here on the street and go to the hotel.'' He led the way to the Ford House and up to his room.

''Jack,'' Stevenson began, ''if I had the sense of one of your mules, I'd have written you these simple instructions and saved you all your trouble and worry. All I have for you is to proceed on down along the Platte, take what pictures seem expedient to you in and about Colorado Springs, Manitou, and the Garden of the Gods, and then double back to Fairplay to meet the rest of us. If you need any supplies, we'll order them today and have them shipped to whatever point you say.''

''Sounds all right to me,'' Jackson acknowledged. ''I'll have to spend the night here and will be back at Acequia by noon tomorrow.''

Then he told Stevenson of the Curtises. ''I plan to visit them tonight. Will you join me? They don't expect me, but I'm sure we'll both be welcome. Suppose I send word that we'll be out after dinner?''

In the comfortable sittingroom of the Curtis home, they whiled away a pleasant evening, talking. Inevitably the conversation led to the mountain of the Snowy Cross.

''And that reminds me, Will,'' George Curtis said, ''I have been trying to spot that mountain definitely for you. I have inquired of everyone who visits the office, for that matter. And I think I have it.''

He went to his study and returned with a large scale map of the Territory. He spread it out on the floor and the three men gathered about it on bended knee.

''Here is Tennessee Pass,'' George explained, pointing to a spot on the map. ''From all that I can learn, the

102

mountain is within shouting distance of the pass. One fellow told me he had seen it from what he called Notch Mountain, one of the sheep backs. You might try that when you get out that way."

"That seems more than likely," Jackson said, "because it jibes with the best information I've been able to secure. I plan to inquire at Fairplay, at Alma, and at Oro until I do find it. I certainly do not intend to let this season pass without photographing that mountain."

Elaine, George and Stevenson, all impressed by that solemn declaration, were confident that the mysterious cross of snow would be revealed to all America within a few short weeks.

Bill was on hand with the horses when Jackson alighted from the train at Acequia at noon the following day. They galloped back to camp to find an eager group awaiting the word from Denver. Jackson assured them the work of the next few days would be quite easy on the feet and nerves, and transmitted the information he had been given by Stevenson. Never before was the Photographic Division made ready for the trail in such short order. By one o'clock, dinner had been consumed, tents were struck, packs loaded and lashed and the march resumed toward the headwaters of the Platte.

Two days later, on the first of July, Jackson and his men were in a cameraman's paradise—the Garden of the Gods. The awe-inspiring red rock formations compelled Jackson to set to work with such zest that he was able to make far more wet plate exposures than he had ever before been able to chalk up as a day's work.

The tower of Babel, Montezuma's Temple, Steamboat Rock, The Kissing Camels, the Seal and the Bear, Balanced Rock, the Mushrooms—all were targets for Jackson's camera. All those exposures called for more hours to get them developed. Well into the night, Jackson labored at his task. To permit himself to work uninterruptedly, he had contrived to draw the black bean, which meant he would function as camp guard for the evening; all the others went to nearby Colorado Springs to sample the diversions this spic-and-span new little city had to offer.

Oh Yankee Doodle is the tune
Americans delight in;
'Twill do to whistle, sing or play,
And just the thing for fighting.

And then on Independence day
(And who's a better right to?)
We eat and drink and sing and play
And have a dance at night, too.

Jackson had planned on making some pictures in
Cheyenne Canyon and getting some views of Pike's Peak
from Cheyenne Mountain before starting on the trip to
Fairplay. Again fate intervened, this time through the
recurring cussedness of the mules. It could have been
Gimlet, the strategist, who ambled away from the picket

line in the early morning hours of the third of July leading the five other scheming little tricksters. Even two of the horses succumbed and pranced off.

Potato John, always the first one up, was the first to note the absence of the animals. Dutifully, he proceeded to the tents of Bill Whan and Tom Cooper, jerked the blankets off them and uttered a laconic "mules gone agin."

Grumbling, swearing and philosophising on the cunning of mules, Tom and Bill threw on what few clothes they did not take to bed with them, gulped down a couple of John's biscuits soaked in syrup, and still calling forth lamentations on their erring charges, started out in search of them. Since no other regular duties could be performed until the absentees were rounded up, other members of the party went to aid the unlucky packers. Jim, Ned, and Lt. Carpenter mounted three of the remaining horses and set off in different directions. Jim headed toward Manitou; the Lieutenant lit out for Cheyenne Canyon; while Ned, the most experienced horseman of the trio, followed the lower road into Colorado Springs. He reasoned that the animals would not do any unnecessary climbing and were apt to seek out the lush grass on the river bottoms of the Fountain. In due time, he noted signs indicating that Tom and Bill had reasoned similarly. It was easy for him to follow their tracks. Soon he chanced upon a little corral and noted Girlie and Polly securely ensconced therein. A tousel-headed ranch lad was perched on a gate rail, solemnly surveying the two little mules. He turned his eyes defiantly toward Ned when he approached.

"Hello there, young fellow," Ned called out. "Looking after our mules for us, I see."

" 'Tain't yer mules," retorted the boy.

106

"Well, maybe they aren't mine, personally," Ned explained, "but they belong to the Survey party I'm with."

"Don't believe it, nary one bit," the boy shot back. "These here critters belongs to a couple o' fellers named Tom and Bill. They cum by a while back and asked paw could they tie 'em up here for a spell 'til they gets back. Promised me a quarter ifen I watch 'em good." With definite finality he added, "Nobody ain't gonna take 'em 'til they gets back, neither."

Ned laughed at the lad's show of determination. "Why, son, I'm not going to try to take the mules. I'm hunting for Tom and Bill to help them corral the rest of the animals."

"You know them fellers?" The boy scrutinized Ned critically.

"Why, of course I do," Ned assured him. "They're packers with our party and it's their duty to round up the mules when they run away. They got started an hour or so ago and I'm trying to catch up with them."

"W-a-a-l, that sounds purty good," the lad conceded. "Guess maybe yer a square shooter."

"Where did they go?" Ned asked, now realizing he was losing valuable time.

"That-a-way," replied the lad, pointing off to the northeast toward the Fountain River. "That's them," he shouted, as he caught sight of mules and horses and riders emerging from a small thicket. "By golly they got 'em all—four mules and horses, just like they said."

"I'll go help them," Ned called out as he galloped off.

"Ho, there, boys," he called. "Glad you've got the little devils." He wanted to laugh at the sorry sight of two burly packers driving before them two sets of horses and mules with the halter ropes tied together to prevent

107

further escape, but one glance at the set expressions on the faces of Bill and Tom made Ned feel that a laugh would be quite out of order.

"I'll get the other two," Ned suggested, "and have them ready when you come up. The kid will be waiting for his quarter."

He galloped back to the ranch where the boy, seeing that Tom and Bill were returning, was leading Girlie and Polly out of the corral.

"Here, you c'n take 'em now," he said as Ned galloped up and dismounted.

"Thanks, son," Ned replied and took the ropes in his hand. "You did a great job of taking care of them. I'll wait here until you get your quarter."

They stood there in awkward silence for a few moments until Tom and Bill arrived with their runaways.

"All right, boy," Tom said, "here's your two-bits. Yu done right well. Hope yer around ifen we looses our stock again."

"Thanks, Mr. Tom," the boy replied. "Ifen yu need me, just holler."

"What'll we holler?" Bill inquired.

"Oh, just yell Jed. Jed White's my name." By now the boy had assumed the attitude of manly importance with thumbs looped in the straps of his overalls.

"We'll do that, Jed," Tom promised as the little group of men and animals started away. "So long now."

Not a word of criticism came from Jackson or a quip from Coulter as the sorry expedition ambled back into camp. The packers, caught for the second time in less than three weeks with their mules gone, offered no excuses. Ned winked at Jackson with a better-lay-off warning and Jackson returned the wink, indicating he understood the situation perfectly. Coulter, with that bright, far-away look of his, was storing up his quips for future use.

Carpenter and Jim rode in later in the afternoon, after combing miles of territory almost to Woodland Park, relieved to see the objects of their search carefully and securely tied to a picket line which Tom and Bill had reinforced with grim determination.

Jackson announced that since the work for that day had been stopped, they would spend one more day in and around Manitou Springs. After that—eighty miles to Fairplay.

On the afternoon of the Fourth of July the full Photographic Division assembled at the camp in the Garden of the Gods and made ready to start the hike to Fairplay. Jackson took time to finish a letter to Emilie.

"And now, my darling," he wrote, "we are off on the final leg of our summer's work. Three more days should find us in Fairplay where we are to meet the Doctor and all the divisions of the Hayden Survey. A few days there in final preparation and we'll be heading into Tennessee Pass in a do-or-die effort to locate and photograph your precious mountain. It will be good to see all the boys again, to finish our 1873 project in grand style and then to hasten back to the sweetest girl under God's heaven."

He signed the letter: "Your most devoted and jubilant, Will," sealed it, and for a moment pondered over the best and quickest way to send the letter on its long journey. A small group of mounted men was just passing camp in the direction of Colorado Springs. Jackson approached them and inquired:

"Would one of you gentlemen be kind enough to post this urgent letter in town for me?" He held the letter aloft. "Unfortunately we are proceeding north and it

109

will be a few days before it can be mailed from any post office along our route."

"Mr. Jackson," one of the party replied as he reached down from his horse and accepted the letter, "it will be a rare pleasure to be of assistance to you. Rest assured it will be posted immediately upon our arrival in the Springs."

Jackson recognized the man as one who had been an interested observer when he had been so busy making all those pictures in the Garden a few days before. "It is most kind of you, sir," he said. "And greatly appreciated. To whom am I indebted for this service?"

"Palmer, William H. Palmer, Mr. Jackson. I'm connected with the Rio Grande Railroad."

"General Palmer!" Jackson exclaimed in astonishment. He recovered from his surprise sufficiently to thank the General again and to express the high honor he felt at meeting the great railroad builder.

"Thank you, Mr. Jackson. I, too, feel deeply honored at meeting and serving, in a very small way, the man who has done so much to permit America to see in pictures the great wonders of the West. I trust we may meet again— when neither of us is as pre-occupied as we are today."

Coulter approached to announce that everything was ready for the march.

General Palmer started off. "I'll be interested in your progress, Mr. Jackson. Will you be kind enough to be my guest at Glen Eyrie when you come this way again?"

"Thank you, sir. I shall be delighted," Jackson called back.

Coulter was bug-eyed when he learned the identity of the man to whom Jackson had been talking. "Jack," he said, "I'll bet if I stick around with you much longer

I'll see Grant, himself, pop out of nowhere to slap you on the back and renew acquaintance.''

Jackson laughed, ''Just for that complimentary remark, Tom, I'll let you ride up front with me now. Maybe we'll run across a governor or some Cabinet official. Come on.'' He mounted his horse, and as Tom followed suit, he described with his arm the great arc that meant to all in the party, ''Forward, march.'' They were on the trail again.

By late afternoon they had reached the Junction House on the Continental Divide. Here they camped for the night, within seventy miles of Fairplay. That distance would have to be covered in the next three days to meet the other divisions of the Hayden Survey on the seventh. It would not be too hard, for twenty-five miles a day was a normal stretch, if time was not taken out for photographing. Jackson had long since given up any idea of making any pictures on this trek to Fairplay.

Potato John had been briefed on the urgency of this expedition and warned to get the members up early enough to complete each day's mileage. His shrill cry of ''grub pile'' awakened everyone at three-thirty the morning of the fifth. There was much grumbling about just getting to sleep, but the grumbling did not perturb the cook. Breakfast was over in time to have the party on the march just at day break. They made twenty-three miles through Hayden Park and descended along the Platte. They made camp at noon and thoroughly enjoyed fresh milk and eggs purchased from a rancher.

The following morning, Potato John stepped up the ''grub pile'' a half hour to be certain there'd be no waste time. There was none, unless the several long minutes Jackson's men stood around waiting for daylight were counted. The grumbling that morning was terrific. But

111

they made twenty-four miles through Wilkerson Pass and South Park. On that day, Jackson bought for his men from a rancher's wife some apple pies to enhance the noonday meal. Shortly after, every man had pie sickness. All eight men did little else for the rest of the day than to make spasmodic trips from the tents to the camp latrine.

On the last morning out, John's "grub pile" rang out at one o'clock. At first no one seemed to notice the vastly stepped-up time. Not until after breakfast, when Jackson pulled out his watch, did any one realize how early John had shouted his breakfast call. By then all anyone could do, as they stood about waiting for dawn, was to conjure up maledictions against the cook. But, they had fully recovered from the pie sickness and made such good time that they were in Fairplay by eight the morning of the seventh of July. Neither Dr. Hayden nor any other members of the Survey had arrived.

I'm go'n' to lay down my burden
  Down by the riverside, down by the riverside,
I'm go'n' to lay down my burden
  Down by the riverside,
And study war no mo'.

Fairplay, 1873, was a rip roaring, dusty metropolis teeming with freighters, pack trains and horsemen. Ever since leaving Clear Creek Camp, Jackson and his men had been looking forward to this rendezvous for they knew they were to make quite a stay here and every man had planned relaxation and fun. In the following ten days every man in the outfit patronized the stores, barber shops, and restaurants. Pay day, coming simultaneously with Stevenson's arrival in Fairplay, put plenty of money into the pockets of the men to dole out to Fairplay's businessmen. Some work was accomplished during these waiting days, but the men enjoyed considerably more free time than they did on the trail.

The very day the photographic section reached Fairplay, Gannett's division as well as the one headed by Wilson came down from the hills and joined forces. A camp similar to the main one in Denver, from which all divisions had started in May, was set up. Old friends and old rivalries were renewed and tales of the summer's trials and tribulations were told and retold.

Although Jackson allowed his men extensive leeway in the matter of work versus fun, he was a severe taskmaster over himself. During the days of waiting for Dr. Hayden to arrive, he tramped the roads leading from Fairplay and got acquainted with the towns, passes, streams, and peaks for miles around. He visited the lively mining camp of Alma and the ghost town of Montgomery. He climbed Mt. Lincoln from which he secured excellent panoramas and some views of the famous Montezuma mine. Hoosier Pass and Horseshoe Canyon became familiar ground to him. On one of these trips he was given a dog by a sourdough he met up Hoosier Pass. The miner-hermit who had been solo-prospecting for years had plenty of company in his little mountain shack home—six dogs, a dozen cats, and a nanny goat.

"You take him, mister," the old miner had said when he saw Jackson fondling the dog. "He's got plenty o' sisters an' brothers an' his mammy won't miss him."

The dog was christened "Spot" and accepted as a member of the Survey.

114

After Dr. Hayden rejoined his divisions late on the 13th, the tempo of activity took on an accelerated pace. Previous general instructions were now superceded by explicit directions, but before handing out these directions, the Doctor allowed a few days for comparing notes on accomplishments to date and for securing suggestions on future missions. Jackson was glad to have further opportunity for inquiries regarding the Mount of the Holy Cross. Every man he had a chance to talk to, he pestered with questions pertaining to its exact location. He was fortunate in meeting men who had seen it—men who tried hard to give him accurate directions to follow to reach the mountain. He was hourly getting nearer to his goal, he could feel it "in his bones."

William N. Byers, founder of the *Rocky Mountain News,* came down with Dr. Hayden to observe the work of the Survey. "So Mr. Jackson has his heart set on finding the Mount of the Holy Cross," Byers said when Hayden introduced him to Jackson. "That shouldn't be hard. It does exist, as we all know. Many in this neighborhood have seen it and can direct you to it. I'd say, just follow through Tennessee Pass and then start asking and searching."

Jackson thanked Byers and said, "Your advice fits in very well with the information I've been able to gather. I know now that the mountain can't be very far away and I don't intend to let this season pass without conquering it."

Dr. Hayden, seldom given to boasting, added, "That's the spirit all of us in the Survey have, Byers. We just will not wind up the work until we have accomplished all we've set out to do." Then, turning to Jackson, he continued, "This is as good a time as any to outline your remaining work—with a representative of the press on hand. You will cross the Sawatch Range to the Elk Mountain region between Gunnison and the Grand and then wind up the season getting that Holy Cross Mountain once and for all. Plan on having all completed by September 1.''

Jackson looked up suddenly at mention of the date for the end of the season. It was a month earlier than he had thought it would be. Dr. Hayden caught the eagerness in his expression, laughed, and assured him he had not mis-spoken. With a knowing look toward Byers but addressing Jackson, he gravely explained, ''Thought you might want to get back to Omaha for your business at the Agency.''

''Not Omaha, Doctor. We're going to be married in Cincinatti, in October. But,'' he hastened to say before the Doctor might decide to prolong the season, ''I'll probably need that extra time to get ready.''

Jackson saw nothing funny in his remark, but Dr. Hayden shook with laughter.

Bill Whan was transferred from Jackson's party while at Fairplay camp and was sent back to Denver to take over the job of maintaining equipment for the Survey. Jackson was sorry to lose him, but pleased to acquire Harry Bishop as a replacement. Harry, a packer of long experience, knew his horses and mules—and their idiosyncracies—equally as well as Bill.

The departure of Bill and Pat Casey, the one to his new duties in Denver, the other to his interests in Central, called for a celebration. A farewell party was held at Tom Kilduff's Hotel.

The tiny dining room, with no furniture other than one long table and hard-backed chairs, rang with singing, with old jokes retold, and new ones brought up from hiding. Pat was called upon for a speech. He demurred but

116

was hoisted to his feet by Bill and John who were sitting on either side of him and who held him standing with their knees pressed hard against his.

Yielding to the inevitable, Pat began, "Gintilmin, 'tis a pleasure t' be wid yez, an' it ain't no fun lavin'. I niver had so much fun in me life. I like ivery wan o' yez, an' I hope yez likes me." He paused. "Go on wid yer wurk, do as Jackson and the Doctor tells yez; iverything'll be fine. An' write t' me—Patrick Casey, Central City, Territory of Colorado." He gave the name and address haltingly, but with deliberateness, proceeding with, "Come back t' see Old Pat." Tears were welling in his eyes, but he regained his composure and finished with, "God bless yez all."

They all gathered around him, vying for a chance to shake his hand and wish him God-speed. Pat had aptly expressed mutual feelings. Someone started humming the music of "Auld Lang Syne." They went through each verse and began all over again. As the party broke up and the men headed back for camp, the words and the tune lingered on.

Jackson's division "hit the trail" again on July 18. They followed a southwesterly course up the Buffalo Peaks with momentary stops to permit Jackson to make such exposures as he saw fit. The other divisions followed a similar route and often pitched camp together. The goal for all in these first days out of Fairplay was Twin Lakes. Here, a semi-permanent camp was laid out.

A little neck of land, jutting into one of the Twin Lakes, had been assigned to the Photographic Division for setting up camp. The owner of this land showed up as tents were being pitched, identified himself as Elmer Derry and immediately got right down to the business of charges for using his land.

117

"Now I don't mind giving ye the use of my land," he told Jackson, "but, of course, ye'll allow me some recompense. I'll expect twenty-five cents a day per head of stock, two dollars for use of that boat," he pointed to a scow, "a dollar a gallon for milk and five cents apiece for eggs." He studied Jackson intently, awaiting his reply.

Jackson looked over the sage-covered neck of land and wondered if there were a quarter's worth of feed to be found on it. He glanced at the scow and surmised it would probably be worth a couple dollars—as scrap lumber. He knew he was being "took," but resolved to parry in the matter of the amount of take.

"Mr. Derry," he said, "Mr. Stevenson, our business manager, tends to all money matters and he will have to make terms with you. He'll be along tomorrow or the next day at the latest. I trust you will let us remain against his coming."

"Well, yes, I suppose I shall have to," Derry replied reluctantly.

Derry's ranch became home to Jackson and his men for the next several days. During that time, Derry's attitude and that of members of his family softened considerably. Many little favors and gifts were afforded the party before final leave taking.

Those days were most active ones. Jackson photographed the moraine, Mt. Elbert, LaPlata Mountain, the little towns of Oro and Granite. Some of the finest panoramic views he ever took were added to his scores of achievements during the stop-over at Derry's ranch. An accident to Jerry, Jackson's riding horse, had necessitated a change of mounts at Fairplay. The change was Dolly, a white mule, which Jackson had accepted with some misgivings. Now he rode Dolly whenever possible, and learned to prefer her to any horse the Survey could provide. He was happy during these days. He was getting wonderful pictures, getting closer to that mysterious mountain by the hour, and best of all, he would soon be back with Emilie.

Life in the hills, however, would never be complete without some annoyances. A leaky bath pan, for instance, got so bad Jackson attempted his own repairs with unsatisfactory results. In the end, he tossed the thing away and thereafter resorted to using a developing tray for a flat bath. Then again, on Mt. Elbert, the highest peak in the Territory, Mag floundered at her best, and, in floundering, wormed her way deep down under fallen logs.

When her load was finally transferred to Gimlet's sturdy back, that little devil proved that he, too, could be ornery.

A real problem developed when Jackson ran short of glass plates and replenishments failed to show up as expected. Harry had been sent to Granite to try to locate the missing shipment. Jim had ridden up to Alma for the same purpose. Each had returned to report failure. Stevenson was contacted and promised to go into action. Jackson took time off to ride up to Oro to try his luck.

When he rode into that tiny mining settlement, he sought out the general store, knowing it would be doing double duty as the village post office. Across its wide front appeared the large painted letters: ·

GENERAL STORE

H.A.W. Tabor, Prop.
Post Office.

Jackson tied Dolly to the hitching post in front of the store and climbed up the plank steps to the entrance. As he entered, he found the greatest conglomeration of

119

foodstuffs, yard goods, and hardware he had ever before seen in so small a room. Three sides of the store were lined with shelves from floor to ceiling, and the shelves were packed with everything from cracker boxes to dynamite caps. A rough, wooden counter ran the length of one side only. This was loaded with hams, slabs of bacon, cheeses, jars without tops filled with pickles, herring, dried apples, prunes, and the like. Out in the center of the store stood hogsheads, barrels, and boxes, all bearing in chalked letters an indication of their contents—kerosene, sugar, syrup, linseed oil, or crackers. In a corner at the far end of the counter was a wired-off little space with a sign "Post Office."

In a moment, the proprietor entered from a rear door which Jackson judged led into living quarters. He was short and stocky, with frank, brown eyes, dark hair, and a frightening handle-bar mustache. A meal bag tucked in above his pants top served as an apron.

"Welcome, stranger. Tabor's the name. What can I do for you?"

"Glad to know you, Mr. Tabor. My name is Jackson, of the Hayden Survey, and—"

"By the eternal!" Tabor interrupted, clasping Jackson's hand and pumping it vigorously. "I *am* glad to meet you. Heard you people were in these parts. Always glad to serve government men."

Jackson thanked him and remarked that some merchants and other citizens he had to deal with were not of such friendly disposition. He told Tabor he had made the trip up to Oro in the off chance of finding his missing glass plates.

"Sorry, Mr. Jackson. Wish I could tell you they were here, but they aren't." Jackson's face showed his disappointment to such an extent that Tabor felt compelled to say or do something to alleviate it. He cut generous cheese slices from a Daisy roll, reached into a cracker box to draw out a half dozen or more and offered them to Jackson. As he took the food and began eating, a shabby, scraggly-whiskered old man entered.

"Ho, there, Hank," Tabor said in a tone of resignation, "what'll it be this time?"

"Well, Tabor, you can see I need some boots. An' I'm mighty low on grub."

"Got any money?" Tabor asked.

"You know I ain't, Tabor, but I will have. Just stake me once more. Just once. I'm gonna make a strike in a day or two, sure as killin'."

Tabor turned to Jackson. "This goes on day after day," he explained. "If I had a dollar for every prospector I've grub-staked, I could have a grand vacation in Denver."

Tabor faced Hank again and tried to be serious. "All right, Hank, start picking out what you need. But remember, this is absolutely the last time." Aside to Jackson, he said, "I've said that a hundred times, too."

Jackson turned suddenly as he heard the rear door open. A tall, dark-haired woman walked from the doorway into the center of the room. Hank, who had begun to lay aside such stuff as he hoped Tabor would allow him, stopped dead as he saw the woman. Ignoring Jackson entirely, she stepped between Tabor and Hank, folded her arms and glared first at one and then the other. At last she turned fiercely on Tabor and snapped like an animal trainer: "Are you grub-staking this good-for-nothing Hank?"

"Now Augusta, my dear," his frightened expression belied his calm words, "you jump at conclusions. Hank's got a sure strike this time. He'll pay me back in a week."

With a snort, Augusta jerked Hank about to face her and demanded, "Where's your big strike this time, Hank? No lies now!"

"Just offen Tennessee Pass, Mrs. Tabor. I swear it," he answered weakly.

Jackson, standing there watching, thought he had never been more uncomfortable in his life.

"Now you two listen to me," Augusta declared. "Hank, you'll get your stuff, but you're going to put it in writing. Horace, don't stand there gawking! Get some paper and be quick about it."

"But, Augusta," Tabor stopped and cringed. Just then she turned and saw Jackson, apparently for the first time. The lines of her face softened as Jackson doffed his hat.

Tabor was quick to take advantage of this brief respite. "Augusta, honey, I wanted to introduce you to a new friend, Mr. Jackson of the Hayden Survey."

"I am delighted to meet you, Mrs. Tabor," Jackson responded.

Mrs. Tabor extended her hand. "I am very sorry, Mr. Jackson, that you have seen me in such a state. You must know Mr. Tabor is so downright big-hearted that if I don't call a halt, he'll have both of us in the poorhouse. He's a good man, I want you to know, but at times I must use extreme methods to startle him into reality."

While she was explaining, Tabor had slipped around the counter, produced some paper and a pen, and dutifully laid them on the counter before his wife. She excused herself to Jackson, scribbled something on the paper and turned to Hank. The old prospector seemed to realize the storm was over; he was no longer trembling, but faced her eagerly.

"Now Hank," she said gently, "you know I've been very good to you. But you must realize that we can't support all the prospectors in the hills. I want you to sign this. It's merely a promise to pay when you can."

The signing being completed, Mrs. Tabor turned again to Jackson. "Could you remain for dinner, Mr. Jackson?"

"Thank you, Mrs. Tabor, but I am long overdue at camp now." Feeling that she might be offended, he added quickly, "But we'll be fairly close for a few days and I would like to feel free to accept that invitation later."

"You may come any time and without advance notice," she assured him.

Tabor, his usual hearty nature fully restored, ventured to add his warm approval of the invitation. "Once you've tasted Augusta's cooking," he boasted, "you'll want to come back often."

Mrs. Tabor followed Jackson out onto the steps, waving as he mounted Dolly and rode off down the street.

"A remarkable woman," he announced to Dolly. "And that Tabor is quite a man, too."

Mine eyes have seen the glory of the coming of the Lord;
He is trampling out the vintage where the grapes of
wrath are stored
He hath loosed the fateful lightning of his terrible swift
sword,
His truth is marching on.

Glory, Glory, Hallelujah!
Glory, Glory, Hallelujah!
Glory, Glory, Hallelujah!
His truth is marching on.

July slipped by almost unnoticed while the picture making went on day after day. August came in unheralded. As time flew by, frantic efforts were made to keep pace. Jackson, eager as he was to complete the allotted work, was constantly being prodded by Dr. Hayden. If the Doctor was with him, he counseled the value of

125

speed, if he was away, he sent messages to "hurry, you are losing golden opportunities."

At times Jackson was more than a little out of patience over these warnings. He knew, from experience in previous seasons, that the Doctor grew more nervous and even unreasonable as success seemed to be "just around the next turn." To Jackson, in these early August days, it seemed that Dr. Hayden had become more unreasonable than ever before.

Disaster struck with full impact upon the harassed photographer on the tenth. Harry came up breathlessly to Jackson, who was working far in front of the pack animals and their custodians, to tell him that Gimlet had tumbled down and broken many of the plates representing the work of the past several days.

Jackson hurried back, hoping almost against hope that some of his precious pictures had been spared the catastrophe. Soon he came upon Dr. Hayden, standing staring in wrath at a heap of broken glass. A smaller pile of salvaged plates had been made alongside. Hayden turned fiercely on Jackson as he approached.

"What in the name of—" he started to upbraid his photographer, but stopped abruptly when he saw the agonizingly dismayed look on Jackson's face. His tone changed immediately. He could be the most nervous and fidgety of men, but in a crisis, such as this, he could be calm and understanding.

"Jack," he said, "there's just no use crying over spilled milk. Thank the good Lord that some of the plates are saved. As to the others, we'll just have to take time out to do them over." He smiled. "Perhaps it was for the best."

Jackson thanked him for his kindness and sympathy, but felt he could not take the matter so lightly. Suddenly,

126

however, he realized the amazing forebearance exhibited by Dr. Hayden. This man, whom he'd often thought unreasonable, was actually laughing the matter off and telling him not to worry!

"Doctor," Jackson said, "you're a prince to take this so lightly. I'll do what you suggest. And, Doctor—" He felt he had to say something to match the Doctor's show of optimism. "I promise I shall not allow this misfortune to disrupt our time-table."

He was as good as his word. Working more feverishly than ever, he back-tracked to secure again the views represented in the broken plates. The back-tracking was in the nature of over-time, for he managed to stick to the schedule set for advance work as well. He felt inclined to pat Gimlet affectionately after developing these "retakes" and finding them superior to the first efforts.

As he had previously resolved, he inquired of every stranger he met about the exact location of the Holy Cross Mountain. He was fortunate now in meeting the men who had actually seen it. By piecing together all information, he was able to assure himself and Dr. Hayden that, once over Tennessee Pass, a diligent search would locate the mountain.

They crossed Tennessee Pass on the nineteenth and moved down to the headwaters of the Eagle River. A large band of Ute Indians, on an Indian Summer hunting expedition, was encamped close to the site picked for the Survey camp. Jackson and Dr. Hayden sauntered over to talk to the Indians.

They approached the Ute camp with some diffidence, not at all certain that the Indians would welcome them. As they drew nearer, they were aware of many Indians standing silently and sullenly, awaiting their coming. Suddenly one of the Indians, who seemed to be vested with some authority, strode up to them. Instead of raising an arm above his head in token of greeting, he extended his hand after the manner of the white man.

"Welcome, white brothers. I am Ouray, chief of Uncompahgre Utes." With a sweep of his hand he invited them to seats on a great fallen log. That same gesture seemed a signal to the remaining Indians to proceed with whatever they had been doing, for they dropped their stoical bearing and busied themselves about their camp. The two visitors sat on either side of Ouray, telling him their names and explaining their business.

Jackson and Dr. Hayden both knew of Ouray, the great chief—friend of the white man. Dr. Hayden commented on the Utes, how sullen and unfriendly they were, in such sharp contrast to their educated, kindly chief.

Chief Ouray explained that they had all suffered immensely from encroachments of whites and plains Indians alike. As for himself, he had come to the realization that the only hope for his people lay in close co-operation with their white brothers. Slowly and painfully, he had worked desperately to get his people to adopt the white man's ways. Sadly, he acknowledged little success for his efforts.

Inevitably the conversation led to the whereabouts of the mountain with the cross of snow. The lucid directions the chief gave caused Jackson's heart to pound with eager excitement.

"Follow Eagle River one day's march," he directed and pointed northwesterly. "Turn left and climb westward over Roches Moutonnée. The climb will be hard, but you will find your mountain."

In his excitement, Jackson jumped from his log seat, grasped the chief's hand and thanked him over and over again for the clear information. The chief's face showed

128

First photograph of Mount of the Holy Cross.

Panorama from near the Mount of the Holy Cross.

Roches Moutonnée Valley and distant view of Mount of the Holy Cross.

Mount of the Holy Cross.
From the first wash drawing by Thomas Moran
preliminary to making his famous oil painting.

Mount of the Holy Cross.
From the celebrated painting by Thomas Moran.

Mount of the Holy Cross.
From an old woodcut in Hayden's report of the 1873 Survey.

Mount of the Holy Cross.
*From a painting made in 1873 by W. H. Holmes,
artist and scientist of the 1873 Survey.*

Composite photograph representing William H. Jackson's
first view of the Mount of the Holy Cross.

Original photo by W. H. Jackson, with cloud effect by Clarence S. Jackson.

amazement that anyone should be so eager to see a particular mountain.

"Would you mind," asked Dr. Hayden, "if Mr. Jackson made some pictures of you and your people in the morning?"

Chief Ouray pondered a moment before answering. He well knew the superstitions of his people and their antipathy toward any of the white man's magic. Then with characteristic adaptability, he replied, "I cannot ask them to do things against their will. But *I* will stand before your camera. Perhaps others will follow my example."

As early as the sun would permit on the following morning, Jackson was on hand with his camera and obtained some of the best Indian pictures of his career. Ouray's followers, seeing their chief stand boldly before that mysterious little box with its magic eye, soon found themselves, still with some trepidation, following his example. Before the picture making ordeal was over, they seemed to be getting real enjoyment out of it.

When Jackson completed his work, the chief offered to have his party accompany the white men to the point where they were to turn westward. The almost boyish eagerness exhibited by Jackson in accepting this aid started a trace of a smile to spread over Ouray's face.

The march along the Eagle proved one of the most pleasant of the entire summer. Lt. Carpenter and Cole accompanied the lead hunters of the Utes and by mid-morning had a plentiful supply of game to add to John's larder. Dr. Hayden rode with Chief Ouray and Jackson and Gardner followed. Everybody rode. Even Ned had a mount, an additional mule, which had been allotted him in Fairplay.

When they arrived at the spot designated by Chief

Ouray, they decided to pitch camp there. Ouray, however, explained that it was necessary for his party to move on. With an exchange of good wishes, the Utes moved on up the narrow valley, their new white friends watching their progress until they disappeared from view.

Climbing over the Roches Moutonnée the following day proved a terrific job. Fallen trees, strewn in terrible confusion over the mountain side, formed nearly impassable obstacles. Dr. Hayden's party did yeoman work in trail blazing, chopping a semblance of a path through the standing timber. Jackson's group followed some time later, since Jackson was forced to stop frequently to make pictures. When finally the spot was selected for camp, most of the men were busy lugging Gardner's clumsy gradienter as far up the mountain as they could before nightfall. Incessant rain hampered operations all day, and Potato John was hard put to prepare a meal.

The morning of the 23rd broke clear but cold. Dr. Hayden's party continued on up the mountain they had begun to scale the previous day. Jackson, Coulter, and Tom Cooper attempted an adjacent peak—Notch Mountain. Coulter carried the plate boxes, Tom the heavy camera, and Jackson the chemicals and precious orange tent. This was definitely not a climb for mules. They dared not walk over slippery logs—scotching was much safer. When they passed through underbrush, they were deluged with icy-cold water. A little of this and they were soaked to the bone. Jackson, patrolling to the front, kept far in the lead of his two assistants. After reaching timberline, he found the going easier. He paused frequently to make sure Coulter and Tom were still following. When their grunting and swearing indicated they were, he would resume his climb.

130

Finally he reached the very top. Desolation, jagged, slippery, slate colored rocks, nothing else. The low-hanging mist prevented any visibility beyond a few feet. And he had worked himself almost to exhaustion to see this! He sat down to await the arrival of his friends. The biting wind soon forced him to extract the tent from his pack and to wrap it about his body. Glumly, he gazed about. If only that infernal mist would lift itself so that he could see something but rocks. And what would he see if it did? He had followed Ouray's directions explicitly. Could that kindly old chief have been wrong? If those confounded clouds would only part—just a little—he could assure himself, be positive. Yet that wouldn't help a particle—couldn't take a picture without the camera and plates. And why hadn't he thought to bring some food?

Suddenly a crashing clap of thunder brought him to his feet. The mists began to swirl, wider and wider grew the little rift in the clouds. Now he could catch a glimpse of a neighboring mountain—the one Holmes and Gardner were on. The opening in the clouds drifted downward. Snow. He could see snow! First a great downward shaft from the very top of the mountain. Then the majestic cross arms and the elongated main shaft. It *was* the Cross!

He stood transfixed. There was his blessed mountain in all its magnificence. Unknowingly, he removed his hat and bowed his head humbly. Tears welled in his eyes. He dashed them away and focused his gaze again on this miraculous symbol. And while he gazed, the clouds folded together again—a curtain closing before a wondrous spectacle.

For some time he stood there staring. Then he recovered sufficiently to make notes on the angle from which he had seen the cross of snow. He arranged some of the smaller rocks to give himself an immediate bearing should the clouds break again. Then he sat down again and continued peering into the fog, a deep feeling of content stealing over his cold body. He had found his mountain! The great task Emilie had set for him had been completed. No pictures yet, but what of that? Making those exposures now would be merely incidental.

From far down the mountain side he heard a faint, "Hallo, Jack." He leaped to his feet, and cupping his hands before his mouth, called, "This way boys. Just a little farther." In his rapture at seeing the cross, he had forgotten Coulter and Tom completely. Now he hurried down toward them. He found the two just on the verge of giving up the attempt. Relieving them of part of their loads, he led the way back to the top. At one of their frequent halts for rest, Jackson peered into the unending mist in an effort to detect any break in the clouds.

His startled cry of "Look!" jarred his companions out of their weariness. He pointed downward toward the valley. There they saw two rainbows in juxtaposition forming one complete circle. All three stood and marvelled, too enthralled by the dazzling sight to speak.

Coulter finally found his voice to remark about "wasting all those beautiful colors on a God-forsaken place like this."

Jackson, who had told them nothing of the spectacle he had been privileged to see, wondered if Coulter would refer to the region as "God-forsaken" after he, too, had glimpsed the snowy cross. As suddenly as it had appeared, the rainbow was again obscured by the shifting fog. At the top, the weary men rested and waited. Jackson hoped fervently that the clouds would part again

132

and allow his friends a view of the magnificent sight that had thrilled him. Coulter and Tom just waited.

When Jackson was convinced that there was no possible opportunity of securing pictures that day, all equipment was safely cached under a protruding rock and the three descended to timberline for the night. Here, they built a great fire and spent the weary hours of night by it. On the opposite mountain, they could see the fire built by the topographical party. All through the night calls between the two groups echoed in the valley between them. Neither party had achieved its objective; the men of both took some consolation in that. The rain had stopped. The air was crisp and cold. In spite of the vast odds against any restful sleep, they all managed to get a few "cat-naps" before morning.

With no breakfast the next morning, the men dragged stiff, sore, and aching bodies up the slopes of the mountains to complete the unfinished business of the previous day. For a great part of the climb, the two parties were within sight and hearing of each other. The jibes of one served to spur on the other.

The cold night had left only flint-hard, glistening ice. Even before chancing a glance toward the Mount of the Holy Cross, Jackson and the others concerned themselves with securing a sufficient amount of water for preparing and developing plates. Fortunately they soon located a hole in a boulder which had collected ice-covered water.

Jackson was amazed that neither of his companions had noted the Holy Cross, now literally staring them in the face. It was time, he thought, to give them the thrill of their lives. He strode to the "direction finder" he had laid out in the rocks the day before. Again, hat in hand, he stood in reverence looking at the Holy Cross.

Coulter was the first to notice Jackson's behavior; he moved over, following Jackson's gaze. Instantly, he, too, was transfixed. He removed his hat and bowed his head. For once this irrepressible fun-maker was at a loss for words.

Tom, in good time, took notice of his friends and out of curiosity, joined them. As he caught sight of the Cross he whispered, "Godawmighty! That's what we cum for, ain't it?"

His remark broke the spell.

"And it's best we get busy on what we came up here for," Jackson said quietly. "But I might as well tell you both, now, that I was treated to a preview of this phenomenon yesterday afternoon. I didn't want to tell you, for I wanted to see what effect it would have on you when you came upon it unexpectedly. And there's something I failed to note yesterday. What do you make of that snow figure down there?" He pointed to a snow mass, collected about half way down the slope to the right of the cross. Before either Tom or Coulter could formulate words, he gave his own version.

"I would like to believe it represents the Madonna raising her hands in supplication toward the cross. This is truly a shrine for all Christendom."

Both Tom and Coulter agreed. Quite out of character, it seemed, Tom was the one who suggested that they complete the work of photographing "before them clouds come up agin."

Never was Jackson so over-joyed. He worked calmly and with dispatch, humming, while so occupied, hymns most appropriate for such an occasion. Funny, he thought, how so many quotations from the gospel ran through his mind on this glorious Sunday morning.

"I shall lift up mine eyes unto the heavens." "Go

134

ye forth unto all the nations." "Ask and it shall be given thee."

How proud Emilie would be! He could hardly wait to see her face when she heard he had succeeded.

Jackson made eight plates that bright Sunday morning. One of these exposures was destined to become perhaps the best known photograph in America.

When the plates were developed, the three men, buoyed up by the inner satisfaction that comes from work well done, joyfully shouldered the photographic equipment and made their way down the steep mountainside.

Already Jackson's thoughts were far away. The job here was finished; he would soon be with Emilie. Even saying the words to himself made him excited and eager. And then, before long, it would be October eighth, the most important day of his life—the day Emilie would become his bride. He smiled to himself—his load was no longer heavy. The steep path led to Emilie.

Clarence S. Jackson, the son of William
H. Jackson, is himself a photographer
and, as an artist for Hopwood Studios,
does western scenes and murals. He has
written various articles and stories of
the west, and a book, *Picture Maker of
the Old West*, published in 1947.

Lawrence W. Marshall is Vocational Co-
ordinator at East High School in Denver. He served as lieutenant colonel in
the infantry. He plans, as does Mr.
Jackson, to write other books on the
pioneer west. At present he is president
of the Colorado Council of American
Pioneer Trails Association.

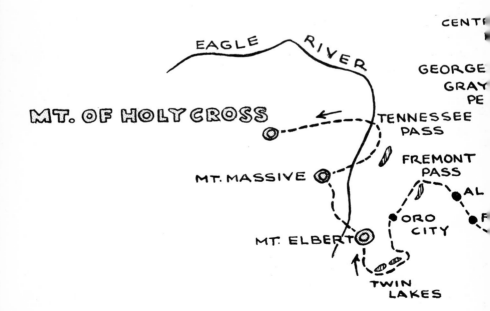

Route of Photographic
Party of Hayden Survey
of 1873

ROUTE

RIVERS

LAKES

RAILROADS

PEAKS

CENT

EAGLE RIVER

GEORGE
GRAY
PE

MT. OF HOLY CROSS

TENNESSEE
PASS

FREMONT
PASS

MT. MASSIVE

AL

ORO
CITY

F

MT. ELBERT

TWIN
LAKES